FAMOUS HYMNS

With Stories and Pictures

By

ELIZABETH HUBBARD BONSALL

Second Edition
Revised and Enlarged

THE UNION PRESS

PHILADELPHIA

Dedicated to my children
Betty, Ann, and Mary
who love these hymns and stories

First Printing, June, 1923
Second Printing, October, 1924
Third Printing, December, 1926
Revised Edition, November, 1927
Fifth Printing, January, 1930
Sixth Printing, November, 1931
Seventh Printing, November, 1935
Eighth Printing, February, 1939
Ninth Printing, December, 1939
Tenth Printing, November, 1940
Eleventh Printing, October, 1941
Twelfth Printing, October, 1942

FOREWORD

———

THESE hymns, with the pictures, were collected a few at a time for my own children. For some time previously I had been trying to have them learn our splendid hymns, especially to sing on Sunday evenings, around the piano. But except for the few hymns which they already knew they preferred to sing from some song books they had, which were illustrated. Then it occurred to me that if the hymns were accompanied by pictures, they would have the same appeal to the children as the other song books. The attempt far exceeded my fondest hopes, the only difficulty now being that the children want to sing the book through from cover to cover every Sunday. And this has been true of other children besides my own.

It is truly a mistake to think that children do not enjoy and appreciate the best. They do, especially if it is presented within the range of their understanding. And there is nothing that excels our hymns. Our greatest poets, such as Longfellow, Lowell, and Whittier, have given us some of their finest work in the form of hymns, and our most famous musicians, as Handel, Mendelssohn, and Beethoven, have written music which has been most fittingly adapted for use as hymn tunes.

It is surprising how the spirit of the hymns has been carried out in paintings by the great Masters. Raphael, Leonardo, Michelangelo, Correggio, Murillo, Millet, and many others found their greatest inspiration in religious subjects such as are expressed by the hymns. It has been a fascinating study to select, from among so many, the very best picture for each hymn.

And then, too, there is a wealth of interest connected with the writing of the words of nearly all the hymns. Some were written in prison, and in times of persecution; some were written as poems for special occasions; some to teach great Christian truths; and others for divers reasons, such as to keep little boys out of mischief, while they were marching, by giving them something to sing!

It is so easy for children to learn while young, and what is learned in childhood will be retained for life. How important it is that we should put the best we have before our children! Any boy or girl who has fond associations connected with the singing of hymns in the home cannot help but have a strong moral support in any time of temptation.

FOREWORD TO THE SECOND EDITION

IT has been gratifying to know that these hymns and pictures have been meeting many different needs. Letters from mothers, from teachers in public schools, kindergartens, and Sunday schools, from superintendents and pastors, have testified to their value in the work they are doing. One little girl of seven knows the name of every hymn in the book by the picture opposite. An Epworth League is using this volume as the basis for the worship service of its meetings. It is being used also for special reference in courses on Religious Art in some of our colleges. As this new edition is being sent forth it is with the hope that it may be the means of still further increasing interest in the thoughtful use of both hymns and pictures.

CONTENTS

Alphabetical List of Hymns

LIST OF ILLUSTRATIONS

HOW OUR HYMNS HAVE COME TO US

PEOPLE have always loved to sing. It seems to be a natural way of expressing happiness. Perhaps you have felt like shouting for joy when you have climbed to the top of a hill, or felt the wind in your face. Or, maybe, when you have heard some steady rhythmic sound, as when you were pounding with a hammer, you may have found yourself humming a tune as you worked. Possibly in some such way as this the earliest songs arose. Of course, they would be very simple at first, but as time went on they gradually became longer and less crude.

Songs of praise to the gods are among the very earliest writings that we have. The singing of hymns was the largest part of the old Egyptian ritual. Four times a day, at sunrise, noon, sunset, and at midnight, the priests chanted regularly the praises of their gods. It is not unlikely that Moses became familiar with these hymns. You remember how he was brought up by Pharoah's daughter and was given an Egyptian education. Knowing about these songs probably helped him later on to write poems to the One True God, the God of Israel.

In the time of Moses we first find the Hebrews using sacred songs. When the Israelites crossed the Red Sea, freeing themselves from Egyptian bondage, Moses and Miriam gave them a song of praise:

> I will sing unto the Lord, for he hath triumphed gloriously;
> The horse and his rider hath he thrown into the sea.
> The Lord is my strength and song,
> And he is become my salvation: etc.   (Exodus 15.)

This is probably the oldest choral song we have, and it is one of the best. It is thought that Moses and the men upon one side sang one line, and were answered by a line from Miriam and the women on the other side.

The Hebrews used singing only for the worship of Jehovah. It seemed like a sacred thing to them. For this reason the songs of the Hebrews ranked far above those of any other ancient peoples.

You all know of the shepherd boy, David, who slew the giant, Goliath. You have admired his courage and bravery, but do you realize that among his greatest gifts to us are the songs which he composed? When he was out on the hillsides, taking care of the sheep, he had plenty of time to look around at the wonders of the earth and sky. In the beauty of nature he saw the glory of God, and expressed his feeling in songs which are found in the Psalms. You are surely familiar with a number of them, but perhaps you have not thought of them as songs before. Doesn't it add to their interest when we think how many thousands of years these same songs have been used?

When David became king, he was so fond of music that he encouraged the people to sing more. There became a greater need for singing in the Tabernacle service. The Bible tells us that there was a great choir trained, formed from thousands of musicians chosen from among the Levites. And when David's son, Solomon, built the Temple, the music became even more magnificent. Do we wonder that the Jewish people have always loved their city of Jerusalem?

From this time on, in the Jewish schools sacred music was studied regularly. But the Hebrew people had hard times ahead of them. Their enemies came upon them and burned their city, leaving the Temple in ruins! Many of the Jews were carried away as captives to Babylon. When asked to sing, they refused. How could they be joyful when they were away from the land their God had given them, and His Temple was in ruins?

> How shall we sing the Lord's song
> In a strange land?
> If I forget thee, O Jerusalem,
> Let my right hand forget her cunning, etc.   (Psalm 137: 1–6.)

But when they returned from captivity they started to sing again. How happy they must have been to be back in Jerusalem once more!

In the time of Christ the ritual of the Temple was almost as elaborate as in the days of Solomon. A large choir of Levites led the worshipers in their praise. Upon each day of the week certain psalms were sung. Upon special festivals there were other psalms, while the priests blew upon their trumpets, and all the people bowed in worship. We can imagine how wonderful it must have seemed to the boy Jesus when he went to the Temple for the first time! He must have been impressed that His Father's house was a house of prayer.

Like other Jewish boys, Jesus was taught to sing the psalms. The hymn which was sung at the Last Supper was probably Psalm 115.

After the Ascension of Christ His followers undoubtedly used the Jewish hymns for some time, but gradually they began to have songs of their own. Passages which we find in our Bible were probably used as hymns; some of them are still in use. Aged Simeon's words found in the second chapter of Luke, verses 29–32, "Lord, now lettest Thou Thy servant depart in peace, etc." were sung in evening worship. This has been called the Evening Hymn, or *Nunc Dimittis*, from the Latin words with which it began. Also the Song of the Virgin Mary was used, found in the first chapter of Luke, verses 46–55, "My soul doth magnify the Lord," called the *Magnificat*.

But, unfortunately, the followers of Christ were not allowed to sing their songs in peace very long. Enemies of Jesus were alarmed at the great increase in the number of Christians, and decided to persecute and imprison them, hoping that they would give up following Christ. It was, indeed, an anxious time for the Christians. They had to meet in little groups in out-of-the-way places—even in caverns under the ground. And yet we know that they met and *sang* and their numbers increased! How we wish we might know just what songs they sang to give them such courage! But we have no record, as they had to be very careful what they wrote for fear of being imprisoned. The Roman historian, Pliny, wrote a letter to the Emperor Trajan about this time, in which he says that the Christians would meet and offer praise to Christ as God. Possibly they sang some such hymn as, "When Morning Gilds the Skies," with the spirited refrain which occurs so often, "May Jesus Christ be praised."

In course of time the persecution of the Christians lessened. Then more and more hymns were written. But only one has come down to us from this early period, and that is supposed to have been written by Clement of Alexandria, about 220 A.D. It has been translated very beautifully, "Shepherd of Tender Youth."

Later on a number of Greek scholars wrote hymns, some of which are now in use. They were very fond of writing about the birth of Christ and His resurrection. One of these has been translated and is included in this book, "The Day of Resurrection."

During this same period some hymns were written in Latin, as the Church became more powerful in Rome; and for nearly one thousand years most of the hymns were written in this language. The writers were also fond of writing of the life of Christ, and the joys of the future life. Many of these hymns are used now and are very familar. "Jerusalem the Golden," by Bernard of Cluny, is one of the best known; also the Easter hymn, "Jesus Christ Is Risen Today."

The next great period of hymn writing is the German. There are more hymns in this language than any other, for the people have always been music-loving. They not only enjoy listening to the music of others, but they want to sing themselves. Great choruses have always been popular in Germany. When the Roman Church discouraged the people themselves from singing in the church service, they determined they would sing outside, at festivals, on pilgrimages, and upon other occasions.

Then came Luther, and the beginning of the Reformation. Against the wishes of the Roman Church, he gave the people the Bible in their own tongue, and he also gave them a hymn book, as has been said, "So that God might speak directly to them in His Word, and that they might answer Him in their songs."

Luther's hymns were of the greatest help in spreading his teaching, for the people loved to sing. It has been said that the whole people sang itself into his doctrine. His greatest hymn, "A Mighty Fortress Is Our God," was soon known to the whole body of Protestants, and inspired them with great courage. It has been called "Luther's Hymn," and at one time the very singing of this hymn was cause for imprisonment. But the hymn became more popular than ever. We have few hymns written by Luther, but those that we have are especially fine, for he was very particular to write only his best.

At about this same time, in France, Clement Marot translated the Psalms, and they were widely sung to ballad tunes. But as the Roman Church started to persecute Marot, he escaped to Geneva, Switzerland. Here he published the famous Geneva Psalter, in 1543. It was translated into many languages and has probably been used more than any other book of praise, except the Psalms themselves. Perhaps we do not realize how many of our well-known hymns today are based upon the Psalms. "The King of Love My Shepherd Is," and "O God, Our Help in Ages Past," are good examples.

How many people know that the very first book printed in America was a psalm book, called the *Bay Psalmist*? The Pilgrims had brought with them from Holland an edition of the Psalms, and this is referred to when

> Amid the storm they sang,
>   And the stars heard and the sea.

Governor Bradford wrote that, when the Pilgrims first landed, "they fell on their knees and blessed the God of Heaven." This same book was used in their devotions. And again the reference is made by Longfellow, when John Alden

> Heard as he drew near the door the musical voice of Priscilla
> Singing the Hundredth Psalm, the grand old Puritan anthem,
> *   *   *   *   *   *   *   *
> Open wide on her lap lay the well-worn psalm-book of Ainsworth

We now come down to our modern times, when there has been a tremendous development in hymn writing. England has given us some of our very finest hymns. Among the pioneers were Isaac Watts, who has been called the "Father of English hymn writers," and Charles Wesley, who wrote nearly six thousand hymns, many of which we use frequently today. As interest in missions grew, the missionary spirit showed in the hymns which were written, and we have a number of splendid challenges to service, such as "From Greenland's Icy Mountains." Reginald Heber, who went as a missionary himself, was the greatest writer of this period. After this we find a number of women writing hymns. Many of them are among our finest, such as "Nearer, My God, to Thee," and reveal a deep devotional spirit. Other persons, who have not written many hymns of their own, have translated for us some of the best hymns from the Greek, Latin, and German. In this way we are able to understand and sing many of the hymns which have meant much to the whole Christian Church.

Just a few words about our hymn writing here in America. For a long time the people in this country wrote very few hymns. You will remember that the Pilgrims used only the Psalms, and they felt that what they had were good enough. The Friends and many other religious groups did not believe in singing in their services at all. So, although there were many talented men and women in our country, they bent their energies in other directions. But gradually a need was felt for a greater number of religious songs, especially when the hymns of the Wesleys and other English composers became known in this country. Some of the earliest hymns sound very strange to us, for the Puritans thought it was wrong to enjoy one's self, and that we ought to be sober and think of our sinfulness. But later on, especially after the Revolution, the American people began to feel their liberty, and express their joy and freedom in poetry. And when our greatest poets, such as Bryant, Whittier, Longfellow, and Holmes contributed to our hymns, we reached a result of which we may well be proud.

There also has grown up a class of sacred song, termed "Gospel Songs," associated with the work of Mr. Moody and Mr. Sankey. When Mr. Moody was in Newcastle, England, in 1873, preaching to a group of working people, he felt that there was a need for sacred songs set to popular tunes. So he published a little pamphlet containing some original compositions of Mr. Sankey. As these were enthusiastically received, more were written, and soon there were enough to fill a whole book. These songs with their popular tunes could be sung on the street, or at work. At large open-air camp meetings and in evangelistic services they have been used with tremendous effect, and their number has been steadily increasing.

While many people feel that these songs are not to be compared with our splendid hymns, they certainly reach many people who have not been drawn to any church. And they have a heart appeal which brings many to love the Master.

One of the most wonderful things about all these hymns is that they were written by so many different authors, in so many countries, and have been sung by so many different sorts of people. In spite of the fact that the Church is divided into so many groups, the same hymns are used in nearly all of them.

But for us the important thing is the message that these hymns bring to us. How much suffering and persecution have been endured that we might have them! What comfort they have brought to those who are in trouble! What inspiration they have furnished for deeds of courage and missionary enterprise! When we realize all this surely the hymns will mean much more to us, and will serve to bring us closer to the Master.

FAMOUS HYMNS: With Stories and Pictures

Awake, My Soul, Stretch Every Nerve

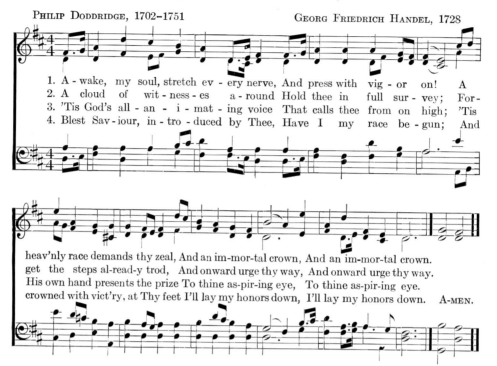

Philip Doddridge, 1702–1751

Georg Friedrich Handel, 1728

1. A-wake, my soul, stretch ev-ery nerve, And press with vig-or on! A
2. A cloud of wit-ness-es a-round Hold thee in full sur-vey; For-
3. 'Tis God's all-an-i-mat-ing voice That calls thee from on high; 'Tis
4. Blest Sav-iour, in-tro-duced by Thee, Have I my race be-gun; And

heav'nly race demands thy zeal, And an im-mor-tal crown, And an im-mor-tal crown.
get the steps al-read-y trod, And onward urge thy way, And onward urge thy way.
His own hand presents the prize To thine as-pir-ing eye, To thine as-pir-ing eye.
crowned with vict'ry, at Thy feet I'll lay my honors down, I'll lay my honors down. A-men.

HAT a stirring hymn this is! Every line is filled with enthusiasm, joy, and vigor. It makes us feel that we must be "up and doing," making each day count for all it is worth.

Philip Doddridge came from a large family. He was the youngest of twenty children. We may well imagine that he did not have an easy life, but had to work for many of the things that he received. As a boy he was given a very thorough Bible training. His mother, an earnest Christian woman, taught him largely herself. There were old Dutch tiles on the wall of the family living-room, which she used for this purpose. He was a very bright boy, and soon attracted the attention of the Duchess of Bedford. She offered to send him to college if he would become a minister in the Church of England. Think of it, an opportunity to be educated by a Duchess! But Philip felt that he wanted to be free to choose his own life-work, so he declined the offer.

He finally entered the ministry, and was known for being the hardest worker and earliest riser in the town. While pastor of a church he taught at the same time in a divinity school, where nearly two hundred students received his training. Besides being a tireless worker for Christ, he wrote many books on religion.

Most of Doddridge's hymns were written as poems with which he ended his sermons. They are based on the Bible passages which he used as his texts. The theme for the hymn above is found in the third chapter of Philippians, verses 13 and 14: "But this one thing I do, forgetting those things which are behind, and reaching forth unto those things which are before, I press toward the mark for the prize of the high calling of God in Christ Jesus."

We are glad that music from Handel, one of our greatest composers, has been chosen for this hymn. It was he who wrote the famous Oratorio, "The Messiah." He was very devout, and while writing his great masterpieces would pray daily for inspiration.

Awake, My Soul, Stretch Every Nerve

John and Peter Running to the Tomb

Eugene Burnand

HOW fast these men are running! They are putting every bit of strength they have into the race. The wind is blowing through their hair, and they are breathing hard, but they do not mind. John is going ahead for he has youth in his favor. See how he is clenching his hands together as he bends forward in his eagerness. Peter is struggling to keep up, though his heart is fairly pounding with the strain.

A short time before, these two disciples heard from Mary Magdalene that Christ was no longer in the tomb! They can hardly believe it—they want to see for themselves. With all possible haste they are running to the sepulchre. Their figures, so full of action, stand out clearly against the early morning sky, and form a decided contrast to the peaceful quiet of the landscape. Every thought is directed ahead, where they are hoping, though they hardly dare express it, for a vision of Jesus.

We feel sure that the artist himself must be a firm believer in Christ when he paints these men so eager to see Him. Burnand's earlier works were of the country life and scenery of his home in Switzerland, but his later pictures have all been of religious subjects. He has tried especially to make Jesus seem very real.

17

Father, We Thank Thee

REBECCA J. WESTON

D. BATCHELLOR

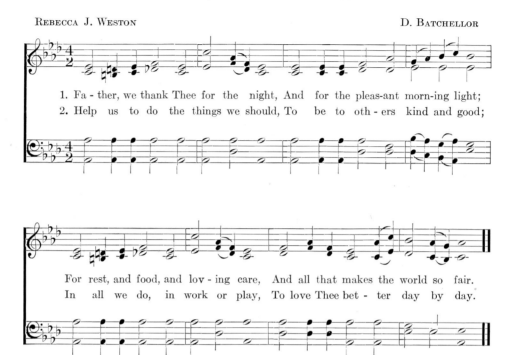

1. Fa - ther, we thank Thee for the night, And for the pleas-ant morn-ing light;
2. Help us to do the things we should, To be to oth - ers kind and good;

For rest, and food, and lov - ing care, And all that makes the world so fair.
In all we do, in work or play, To love Thee bet - ter day by day.

IN the morning when we awake it is such a busy time, I wonder if we always stop for a moment to say "thank you" to God for taking care of us.

This little hymn tells us so beautifully of the things for which we all should be particularly thankful: the night's rest, the daylight, our food and shelter, and the care which our mother and father give to us. And then, besides, there are many other things which each of us has, all our own, for which we should give thanks. So often we just take these things without realizing that they are good gifts from God our Father.

Many Sunday-Schools use this hymn for their opening song. It is dearly loved by the children, and serves as a little prayer as well as a morning song. Not only in Sunday-Schools is it used, but in kindergartens and primary schools all over the country children start their day of school work with this hymn.

* * * * * *

One day Millet, the well-known French artist, was painting a picture in his study, when he happened to glance out of the window. There he saw his wife giving the children their lunch on the doorstep, making a far lovelier picture than the one upon which he was working. So, laying aside his other work, he quickly started this new picture which he saw from his window. Do you see the man behind the house digging in the garden? That is Millet himself, for he wanted to show his own part in the care of the family!

Father, We Thank Thee

Feeding Her Birds
Jean François Millet

AN you imagine a happier family scene than this? The children have been playing around the yard, for we see a little cart and a basket overturned. But as soon as their mother appeared in the doorway with the soup they left their play and ran to sit on the doorstep, waiting their turn to be fed. The hen, too, would like to be included, and is watching for any morsels that may fall. One little girl has brought her doll with her and holds her lovingly in her arms.

Do you suppose that the children are having their lunch or their supper? If you look at the shadows you will see how short they are, and will know that the sun is high in the heavens. It cannot be a very hot day, for see how warmly the children are dressed. Do you notice what queer-looking clothes they wear? Everything they have on has been made at home; even the cloth is homespun. The two little ones with bonnets are girls, while the youngest, in the center, with a cap is a boy. See how lovingly his sister has put her arm around him to help him bend forward for his taste of broth!

In the long winter evenings their father probably made the wooden doll, the little cart, the stool, the wooden bowl and spoon, and even their wooden shoes. Probably the very house in which they live was largely built by him. We are told that this little white stone cottage is still standing, and is nearly covered by the ivy vine which grows by the door.

No wonder these children love their parents, for they know that everything they have— their food, their clothes, and their shelter—comes through them.

When Morning Gilds the Skies

German, 19th Century
Translated by Edward Caswall, 1853

Joseph Barnby, 1868

1. When morning gilds the skies, My heart a - wak - ing cries, May Je-sus Christ be praised!
2. When-e'er the sweet church bell Peals o - ver hill and dell, May Je-sus Christ be praised!
3. The night be-comes as day, When from the heart we say, May Je-sus Christ be praised!
4. In heaven's e - ter - nal bliss The love-liest strain is this, May Je-sus Christ be praised!
5. Be this, while life is mine, My can - ti - cle di - vine, May Je-sus Christ be praised!

A-like at work and prayer, To Je-sus I re-pair; May Je - sus Christ be praised!
O hark to what it sings, As joyously it rings, May Je - sus Christ be praised!
The powers of darkness fear, When this sweet chant they hear, May Je - sus Christ be praised!
Let earth, and sea, and sky, From depth to height reply, May Je - sus Christ be praised!
Be this th' e-ter-nal song Through all the a-ges long, May Je-sus Christ be praised! A-men.

THIS rousing hymn, with its spirited refrain in every third line, attracts us by its unusualness. It is a translation from an old hymn, and is probably very similar to the hymns that were used by the early Christians. We have no way of knowing just what the very first Christian hymns were like. At that time the Christian Church had many enemies who did not understand about Jesus' life and teaching. The Christians were not allowed to meet to hold services, but they gathered in little groups in caverns and secret passages under the ground, outside the cities.

These caverns, or catacombs, are still in existence, and upon the walls there are drawings and writings still preserved for us. For a long time they were safe in these places, but they dared not write their songs, for fear of detection. And yet we know that they sang. Pliny, the Roman historian, tells us that the Christians used to meet in the morning and evening, and sing praise to Christ as God.

And what greater message is there than "May Jesus Christ be praised!" when we praise Him, not only with our lips, but with our lives?

When Morning Gilds the Skies

Song of the Lark

Jules Adolphe Breton

OW happy this girl is as she starts her day of work! The sun is just beginning to appear behind the trees in the distance, where lies the little village. She has made an early start, for she has a long, hard day of work ahead of her. With her sickle in her hand and her apron turned up to her waist, she has started forth to gather heads of wheat. As she is walking down the little path she suddenly hears something which makes her look up. It is the song of the lark singing high in the heavens. The little bird may be seen in the picture if you look closely.

She pauses for a moment in her own song to listen. Though she is but a poor French peasant girl she looks so healthy and full of vigor that we cannot but admire her. Her large hands and feet show that she is used to being out in the sun and wind. We feel sure that she is happy in her work, hard though it may be, for she has learned to love all the wonderful things that God has put around her.

Two great French artists, Breton and Millet, each loved to paint the peasants. Their work is often contrasted, for Millet shows us very plain peasants, hard at work and often tired, while those of Breton are full of joy and vigor.

Work, for the Night is Coming

ANNA L. COGHILL, 1860   LOWELL MASON, 1864

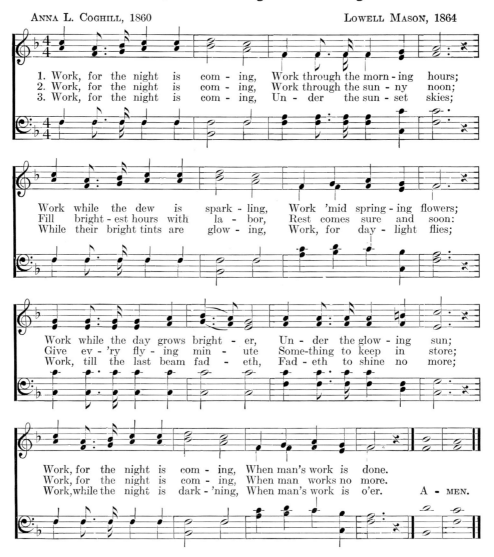

1. Work, for the night is com - ing, Work through the morn - ing hours;
2. Work, for the night is com - ing, Work through the sun - ny noon;
3. Work, for the night is com - ing, Un - der the sun - set skies;

Work while the dew is spark - ling, Work 'mid spring - ing flowers;
Fill bright - est hours with la - bor, Rest comes sure and soon:
While their bright tints are glow - ing, Work, for day - light flies;

Work while the day grows bright - er, Un - der the glow - ing sun;
Give ev - 'ry fly - ing min - ute Some-thing to keep in store;
Work, till the last beam fad - eth, Fad - eth to shine no more;

Work, for the night is com - ing, When man's work is done.
Work, for the night is com - ing, When man works no more.
Work, while the night is dark - 'ning, When man's work is o'er.   A - MEN.

THIS hymn surely calls forth every bit of energy that we have. It is based on the words of Jesus, "The night cometh when no man can work." We are therefore called upon to use to the utmost all the time that we have.

The author, Anna L. Coghill, was a Canadian woman. In her country, so far north, the summers are short. It is particularly important to use every minute in getting the crops started in plenty of season. Otherwise they will not ripen in time, and cannot be harvested before the early frosts set in, and thus the year's work may go without result.

Even the music for this hymn in itself drives us on. The rhythm has such a vigorous swing that we cannot but feel its power. It was written by Lowell Mason, a Boston musician, who did much for promoting music in America. He is remembered chiefly for his many hymn-tunes. Have you ever noticed that the music for "Nearer, My God, to Thee," and "From Greenland's Icy Mountains," has come from this same composer?

22

Work, for the Night Is Coming

The Sower

Jean François Millet

T has been said that all Millet needed to make a great picture was a peasant in a field, and that is what we have before us here. We cannot see the man's features very well, but his work is plain. He is scattering seed in the newly plowed land. In the distance we see the oxen that have prepared the ground which he must cover. The sun has set, but there is still much to be done. Probably he is tired, but he feels that his work must be finished, and he is hastening on with great strides while there is still a glimmer of daylight left.

Millet was brought up a peasant himself. When a boy he loved to draw, but there was little time for anything of that sort in the busy life that the peasants had to lead. But one day he saw an old man, bent nearly double, walking along leaning upon a cane. Something about this old man made Millet want to draw his picture. Taking some charcoal from his pocket, he quickly made a sketch upon a stone wall near by. All who passed recognized the old man, and told Millet that he ought to be a painter. Millet's father was pleased and, hard as it was for him, made arrangements for his son to take some lessons.

Millet always loved the simple life of the peasants. Some people called him a painter of ugliness, and asked why he did not make his peasants good-looking. But he replied that he painted life as he saw it; that beauty was not merely in the face, but in the whole expression.

Jesus, Tender Shepherd, Hear Me

MARY LUNDIE DUNCAN, 1839   JOHN B. DYKES

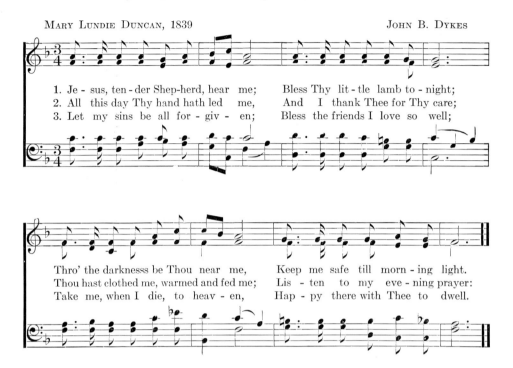

1. Je - sus, ten - der Shep-herd, hear me;   Bless Thy lit - tle lamb to - night;
2. All this day Thy hand hath led me,   And   I thank Thee for Thy care;
3. Let my sins be all for - giv - en;   Bless the friends I love so well;

Thro' the darknesss be Thou near me,   Keep me safe till morn - ing light.
Thou hast clothed me, warmed and fed me;   Lis - ten to my eve - ning prayer:
Take me, when I die, to heav - en,   Hap - py there with Thee to dwell.

PERHAPS this is the very first hymn that you ever learned. Many mothers and fathers use it as a bedtime song for their children. It is really a little prayer. Mrs. Mary Duncan, the wife of a Scotch minister, wrote it just for her own children. We are sure that she must have been a very lovely mother to have such beautiful thoughts. Of course, she had no idea that more people by far would use this hymn than would ever hear of her husband's sermons.

And what a lovely hymn this is! I am sure that we cannot but sleep more peacefully when we think that Jesus is caring for us all through the night.

Dr. Dykes, who composed the music used with this hymn, was a minister as well as a musician. It was his custom to play his compositions before his own family for their criticism before he gave them to the public. They are now sung all over the world.

Jesus, Tender Shepherd, Hear Me

"The Good Shepherd"

Frederic Shields

THESE sheep have nothing to fear while the shepherd is with them; they know he will care for them. Evening is coming on and it is time for them to leave the green pastures, where they have been feeding and playing all day, and go to the fold.

The shepherd calls and the sheep know his voice and follow him. He is taking them to a stream for a last cooling drink, as we see in the picture. The older sheep are eagerly quenching their thirst, but the little lamb in the foreground does not want to get so close to the water. See how he is pushing back against his mother!

Two of the little lambs seem to be tired and the shepherd is carrying them. Do you see at the shepherd's side the sheep looking up at the little lamb? We are sure that it must be the mother. She knows the little ones are safe in the shepherd's arms.

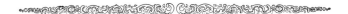

Hushed Was the Evening Hymn

JAMES D. BURNS, 1857   ARTHUR S. SULLIVAN, 1874

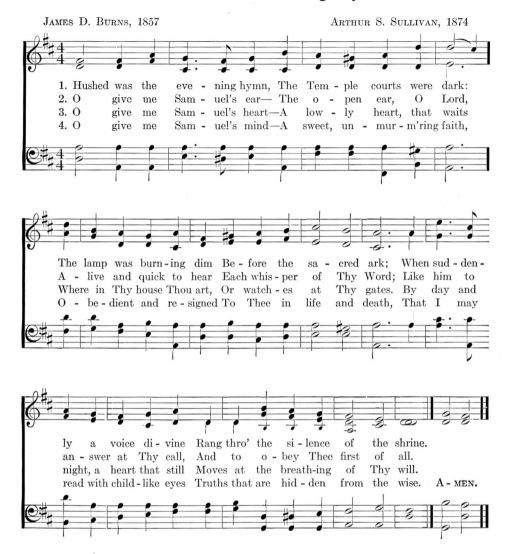

1. Hushed was the eve - ning hymn, The Tem - ple courts were dark:
2. O give me Sam - uel's ear— The o - pen ear, O Lord,
3. O give me Sam - uel's heart—A low - ly heart, that waits
4. O give me Sam - uel's mind—A sweet, un - mur - m'ring faith,

The lamp was burn - ing dim Be - fore the sa - cred ark; When sud - den -
A - live and quick to hear Each whis - per of Thy Word; Like him to
Where in Thy house Thou art, Or watch - es at Thy gates. By day and
O - be - dient and re - signed To Thee in life and death, That I may

ly a voice di - vine Rang thro' the si - lence of the shrine.
an - swer at Thy call, And to o - bey Thee first of all.
night, a heart that still Moves at the breath - ing of Thy will.
read with child - like eyes Truths that are hid - den from the wise. A - MEN.

THIS beautiful little song comes from a collection of evening hymns written by a Scotch minister, James D. Burns. For this collection he wrote thirty-one hymns, one for each day of the month. The hymn above is one of the best and is a particular favorite with the children.

Burns was never very strong. He was forced to give up his work in Scotland and had to travel to Spain for his health, but he did not feel that he could be idle, so as soon as he was able he took a church again, for he felt that he must preach about Jesus.

The music for this hymn was written by Sir Arthur S. Sullivan, the famous London organist. He is well known for his religious music. As the author of "The Lost Chord" and various oratorios, as well as of light opera, he has gained great popularity.

Hushed Was the Evening Hymn

The Child Samuel

James Sant

HEN we are busy, or tired, it is not always easy to answer promptly when we are called, is it? And yet we know how the child Samuel left his bed three times in the night and ran to Eli, the priest, when he thought Eli had called. After the third time Eli told him that it must be God whom he had heard.

In this picture we see Samuel after he has been called the fourth time. He is listening to the voice of the Lord. Instinctively he has clasped his hands and, with his lips parted, looks up with wonder and surprise. What a beautiful picture he makes as the light shines down upon him from above. Dressed in simple night clothing, there is nothing to take our minds from the earnest, uplifted face.

We are not surprised that Samuel later became a great leader of his people. All through his life he listened to the voice of God, and he always obeyed, no matter how hard it might be for him.

Now the Day is Over

S. BARING-GOULD, 1865   JOSEPH BARNBY, 1868

1. Now the day is o - ver,   Night is draw - ing nigh;......
2. Je - sus, give the wear - y   Calm and sweet re - pose;......
3. Grant to lit - tle chil - dren   Vi - sions bright of Thee;......
4. Com - fort ev - 'ry suf - f'rer   Watch - ing late in pain;......
5. Through the long night-watch - es,   May Thine an - gels spread......
6. When the morn - ing wak - ens,   Then may I a - rise........

Shad - ows of the eve - ning   Steal a - cross the sky.
With Thy ten-d'rest bless - ing   May our eye - lids close.
Guard the sail - ors toss - ing   On the deep blue sea.
Those who plan some e - vil   From their sin re - strain.
Their white wings a - bove me,   Watch - ing round my bed.
Pure and fresh and sin - less   In Thy ho - ly eyes.   A - MEN.

1. eve-ning Steal a - cross the sky.

REV. SABINE BARING-GOULD, the English minister who wrote this hymn, was interested heart and soul in his Sunday-school. Some of his best hymns, such as "Onward, Christian Soldiers" and this one, were written with his scholars directly in mind. Baring-Gould felt the need of more evening hymns for children, and wrote this one for them to sing at evening service. It is based on the verses from the book of Proverbs, "When thou liest down, thou shalt not be afraid: yea, thou shalt lie down, and thy sleep shall be sweet."

How beautiful is the music also! Do you notice how the melody is largely upon one note? Yet the ever-changing rich chords in the bass prevent any monotony. Altogether the effect is most peaceful and soothing.

Joseph Barnby, the composer, was an English organist who encouraged the use of better music in religious worship. Many of our best tunes were written by him. In all he wrote nearly two hundred and fifty hymn-tunes.

Now the Day is Over

The Angelus

Jean François Millet

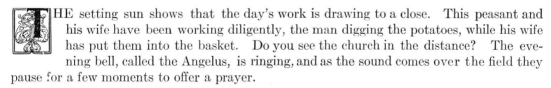

THE setting sun shows that the day's work is drawing to a close. This peasant and his wife have been working diligently, the man digging the potatoes, while his wife has put them into the basket. Do you see the church in the distance? The evening bell, called the Angelus, is ringing, and as the sound comes over the field they pause for a few moments to offer a prayer.

This was the first picture of Millet's to attract notice. For years he had painted, but few cared for his peasants. He was so poor that once he and his wife went without food for twenty-four hours, but his children did not want. Hard as was his life, it was happy. "Better a cottage among peasants than a palace in Paris," was his motto. But with the painting of "The Angelus" people began to realize the message of his pictures, and they were placed in the greatest art galleries. When this one was hung in the Louvre many people in Paris were forgetting God. But this picture served to call the minds of many back to Him.

Millet put so much time and effort into this painting that he said he seemed to hear the bell ringing. At his own request he was buried near the little church which we see in the picture.

Abide With Me!

Henry F. Lyte, 1847   William H. Monk, 1861

1. A - bide with me! fast falls the e - ven - tide, The dark - ness deep - ens;
2. Swift to its close ebbs out life's lit - tle day; Earth's joys grow dim, its
3. I need Thy pres - ence ev - ery pass - ing hour: What but Thy grace can
4. I fear no foe, with Thee at hand to bless; Ills have no weight, and
5. Hold Thou Thy cross be - fore my clos - ing eyes, Shine through the gloom, and

Lord, with me a - bide! When oth - er help - ers fail, and com - forts flee,
glo - ries pass a - way; Change and de - cay in all a - round I see:
foil the tempt - er's power? Who like Thy - self my guide and stay can be?
tears no bit - ter - ness: Where is death's sting? where, grave, thy vic - to - ry?
point me to the skies. Heav'n's morning breaks, and earth's vain shadows flee:

Help of the help - less, O, a - bide with me!
O Thou who chan - gest not, a - bide with me!
Through cloud and sun - shine, O, a - bide with me!
I tri - umph still if Thou a - bide with me.
In life and death, O Lord, a - bide with me! A - MEN.

HENRY FRANCIS LYTE was an English clergyman with remarkable poetic gifts. He started out to spend his life in literary pursuits, but as this soon seemed to him a selfish course he decided to give it up and to serve God by laboring for the poor. Consequently he took a church among a poor, rough, seafaring population on the coast of England.

Lyte loved children, and gathered together a Sabbath school of several hundred scholars. He loved the ocean, and once wrote, "From childhood it has been my friend and playmate, and I never am weary of gazing on its glorious face."

There were many problems which brought sorrow to Lyte's sensitive nature. At one time nearly his whole choir left to join another group. The lines, "When other helpers fail, and comforts flee," may refer to this experience. As his health gave out he was obliged to give up his work. He felt that his life had been a failure, and prayed that he might write something that would live. After preaching his farewell sermon, he went down to the sea-shore alone. The evening was fast closing in when he retired to his study, and an hour later presented his family with the hymn given above. His prayer had been answered. This most beautiful evening hymn is everywhere loved by children, and its meaning deepens as they grow older.

Abide With Me

Reproduced by permission of the publishers, The Medici Society of America, Boston and New York   Jean Baptiste Corot

The Woodgatherer

NO one loved the misty dimness and shadows of the evening more than Jean Baptiste Corot, the great French landscape painter. As a boy he used to look out of his window at night to watch the clouds, the sky, and the trees. Whenever he found time he painted, although his parents wanted him to take up some line of business. When, however, his talent became recognized, his parents gave their consent to have him study art.

For several years Corot studied in Italy, painting landscapes with an occasional temple in the background, or sometimes a few inconspicuous figures of people, or nymphs. But it was the trees which appealed to him particularly; not the massive oak, nor the tall and stately pine, but the shimmering willows, the poplars, and the birches, with the wild flowers beneath them. He loved curved, bent trunks, and used few straight lines in his pictures. Browns, pale greens, and silvery grays were among his favorite colors: but usually a dash of some bright color made a most effective contrast. His works have been called "painted music." We can almost imagine that we hear the birds singing, and the wind rustling the leaves.

Corot is often called the "happy one." His parents were able to provide for him during his period of study, so that he was never in want. Later he lived in the beautiful forest of Fontainebleau, near the peasant artist, Millet. We are told that he always sang, or whistled, like a care-free boy, as he worked. He would get up at three o'clock in the morning, before the sun, to watch the break of day. Then toward evening he would gaze at the falling of the night.

Gradually honors came to Corot, and his works were placed in the finest galleries. As he became successful he was most generous in helping others. When young artists came to study with him, he would accept no pay. Everybody loved him and called him "Pere Corot."

Holy Night, Peaceful Night!

Translated from JOSEPH MOHR, 1818

FRANZ GRUBER, 1818

1. Ho - ly night, peace - ful night! All is dark, save the light
2. Si - lent night, ho - li - est night! Dark - ness flies, all is light,
3. Si - lent night, ho - li - est night! Guid - ing Star, lend thy light!
4. Si - lent night, ho - li - est night! Won - drous Star, lend thy light!

Yon - der where they sweet vi - gil keep O'er the Babe, who in si - lent sleep
Shep-herds hear the an - gels sing: "Al - le - lu - ia! hail the King,
See the east - ern Wise Men bring Gifts and hom - age to our King,
With the an - gels let us sing Al - le - lu - ia to our King,

Rests in heav - en - ly peace, Rests in heav - en - ly peace.
Christ the Sav - iour is here, Je - sus the Sav - iour is here."
Christ the Sav - iour is here, Je - sus the Sav - iour is here.
Christ the Sav - iour is here, Je - sus the Sav - iour is here.

A - MEN.

WHENEVER Christmas carols are sung this hymn is almost sure to be among them, for it has long been one of the best loved. It is over one hundred years old, and comes to us from Austria. It was written for Christmas, by Joseph Mohr, while he was an assistant clergyman near Salzburg. A schoolmaster, Franz Gruber, from the neighboring village of Ansdorf, composed the lovely music with which it is always associated.

What a beautiful little song this is; so short and yet so full of meaning! Do we wonder that some of the greatest singers include it in their concert programs, for they know that it has an appeal for everyone?

We are sorry indeed that we do not know more about the life of Correggio, the painter of the picture on the opposite page. He was born in the little Italian village of Correggio, from which he got his name. He always lived there, never traveling far, and he saw very little art besides his own. Wealth and fame apparently made no appeal to him. In all his works we can see his happy spirit, and his love of the beautiful.

Holy Night, Peaceful Night!

Holy Night

Correggio

O you wonder that this is, perhaps, the greatest favorite of all the paintings of Jesus' birth? What could be more lovely than the beautiful mother and child, with the shepherds attending, and the angels overhead? Although it is early in the morning, and the dawn is just breaking over the hills in the distance, the soft radiance which comes from the baby lights the picture.

What a contrast to the tiny baby is the strong shepherd in the foreground! He seems to have spoken, for his arm is still uplifted as with a gesture; or, is he removing his cap with reverence, awakened by the beautiful scene? The younger shepherd beside him, holding back the dog, is looking up with approval. Are they telling Mary about the vision of the angels? Who is the woman with them, and what has she in her basket? Look closely and you will see the heads of two turtledoves. Perhaps she was on her way to the Temple with her offering, but was attracted by the light in the stable, and came in with the shepherds. The light is so bright that she has put up her hand to shield herself from it.

In the background there are animals dimly outlined. Can you see Joseph holding back the donkey, which is trying to see what strange object is in its manger? Above, in a cloud of glory, are the beautiful angels. They show us that Heaven itself was rejoicing at this event. But our main interest is in the mother with her child. How tenderly she holds the little one in her arms as she kneels beside the manger! There may be angels singing, and shepherds watching, but the thought of the mother is centered upon her baby.

Once in Royal David's City

Cecil F. Alexander, 1848

Henry J. Gauntlett, 1856

1. Once in roy - al Da - vid's cit - y Stood a low - ly cat - tle shed,
2. He came down to earth from heav - en, Who is God and Lord of all,
3. He be - came our child-hood's pat - tern; Day by day like us He grew;
4. And our eyes at last shall see Him, Through His own re-deem - ing love,
5. Not in that poor low - ly sta - ble, With the ox - en stand - ing by,

Where a moth - er laid her ba - by In a man - ger for his bed:
And His shel - ter was a sta - ble, And His cra - dle was a stall:
He was lit - tle, weak and help - less, Tears and smiles like us He knew:
For that child so dear and gen - tle Is our Lord in heaven a - bove:
We shall see Him; but in heav - en, Set at God's right hand on high;

Ma - ry was that moth - er mild, Je - sus Christ her lit - tle child.
With the poor, and mean, and lowly, Lived on earth our Sav - iour holy.
And He feel - eth for our sadness, And He shar - eth in our gladness.
And He leads His chil - dren on To the place where He is gone.
When like stars His chil - dren rise Sing - ing prais - es in the skies. A - men.

EVERYONE loves this beautiful Christmas hymn. The story is told so simply that all children can understand it. It describes for us very clearly the humble place in which Jesus was born, and makes us feel that though He was a King He wanted to share the hardships of the very poorest.

It was written by Mrs. Alexander, the wife of the Bishop of Derry, Ireland. Perhaps you are familiar with her famous poem, "The Burial of Moses." She was a very quiet woman, who wrote most of her hymns as poems for special occasions, never dreaming that they would be published and sung far and wide.

Once in Royal David's City

Nativity

H. LeRolle

HOW different is this picture from other paintings of Jesus' birth! There are no angels with crowns and harps, and the birthplace is not transformed into a garden, or any other beautiful spot. The place is before us in all its simplicity, just a cave stable with rough supports for the roof. At one side we see the donkeys standing by their feeding tubs, while on the opposite side pitchforks are lying on the hay.

The shepherds, with their dogs, have just come in. They are standing half hidden by the pillars, gazing with wonder upon the scene. It seems too sacred and holy for them to go any nearer. One has raised his hand in awe, another has dropped upon one knee, while the youth in the rear is rising on tiptoe for a better view.

In the distance are Mary and Joseph. Mary is looking lovingly at the new-born child, while Joseph turns toward the shepherds who have just come in. They are clothed as simple peasants, and seem just like any other ordinary folks. Yet Mary's motherhood is glorified. The shepherds, though very plain men, are looking on with awe and reverence. We feel that Jesus came in this humble way to glorify the common things of life.

Le Rolle is a modern French artist. He has painted a few religious pictures, but his favorite subjects are large landscapes with few people in them.

Away in a Manger

MARTIN LUTHER

From REV. J. E. SPILMAN

1. A - way in a man - ger, no crib for a bed, The lit - tle Lord
2. The cat - tle are low - ing, the ba - by a - wakes, But lit - tle Lord
3. Be near me, Lord Je - sus; I ask Thee to stay Close by me for -

Je - sus laid down His sweet head. The stars in the heav - en looked
Je - sus no cry - ing He makes. I love Thee, Lord Je - sus, look
ev - er, and love me, I pray. Bless all the dear chil - dren in

down where He lay—The lit - tle Lord Je - sus a - sleep on the hay.
down from the sky, And stay by my side un - til morn - ing is nigh.
Thy ten - der care, And fit us for heav - en to live with Thee there. A - MEN.

T is said that Martin Luther wrote this beautiful little Christmas hymn for his own children. His home life was very happy; he had a remarkable wife, Catherine von Bora, who did everything in her power to help her husband in his work. There were times when the Luther family had very little money. Then Catherine managed a garden, rented parts of their property, and brought up the five children so economically that Luther was able to keep right on in his great task of spreading the study of the Bible.

Christmas was a great event in the Luther household. For weeks ahead Christmas carols were practised, with every member of the family joining in. Then when the day arrived, a few of their dearest friends would gather with them around the Christmas tree, with its pretty decorations and simple presents. Luther would lead the singing, playing at the same time an accompaniment upon the lute.

It seems hard to imagine that anyone so full of energy and power as Luther would be able to write such a lovely cradle hymn as this. We are very glad that we have this little hymn from his pen, for it shows us the tender side of his nature.

Away in a Manger

Adolphe William Bouguereau
Adoration of the Shepherds

HEN we look at this picture we forget we are in a stable, though the rafters, the hay and ropes are all reminders of the fact. Mary has made the little manger as comfortable as possible for the baby Jesus, and with quiet dignity is receiving the shepherds. How proud and happy she is as she lays back the coverlet so that they may have a better view of her baby boy! Joseph is standing in the background as guardian of the little family. He has turned to watch the shepherds, and seems interested in their expressions of wonder.

The shepherds are crowding close. The brilliant light from the baby shines full upon them and the marvel of the scene comes over them. Some have fallen on their knees with clasped hands. The older man in the background instinctively removes his hat. The one holding the little lamb nestles it closer to him.

The shadow in the background and the sacrificial lamb serve to remind us that it is not a life of ease that awaits the baby Jesus. But it is the way in which He later overcame His hardships that makes us love Him and realize that He is truly the Son of God.

The little group before us, however, are entirely unconscious of anything but the presence of the sleeping baby. Upon the faces of all there is the look of joy which shows to us the happiness which the Christ Child brings to the world.

It Came Upon the Midnight Clear

Edmund H. Sears, 1849   Richard S. Willis, 1850

1. It came up-on the mid-night clear, That glo-rious song of old,
2. Still through the clo-ven skies they come, With peace-ful wings un-furled;
3. And ye, be-neath life's crush-ing load, Whose forms are bend-ing low,
4. For lo! the days are has-t'ning on, By proph-et-bards fore-told,

From an-gels bend-ing near the earth, To touch their harps of gold:
And still their heaven-ly mu-sic floats O'er all the wea-ry world.
Who toil a-long the climb-ing way, With pain-ful steps and slow—
When with the ev-er-cir-cling years Comes round the age of gold;

"Peace on the earth, good-will to men, From heaven's all gra-cious King;"
A-bove its sad and low-ly plains They bend on heaven-ly wing,
Look now, for glad and gold-en hours Come swift-ly on the wing;
When peace shall o-ver all the earth Its an-cient splen-dors fling,

The world in sol-emn still-ness lay To hear the an-gels sing.
And ev-er o'er its Ba-bel sounds The bless-ed an-gels sing.
O rest be-side the wea-ry road, And hear the an-gels sing!
And the whole world give back the song Which now the an-gels sing. A-men.

WE should love this Christmas carol doubly well when we realize that it was written here in America. A Boston minister, Dr. Sears, wrote it as a poem, but the next year this joyful music was composed for it, so that now it is included among our hymns.

A minister once remarked concerning it that, no matter how unequal to the great day his Christmas sermon might be, he always felt that the singing of this hymn made up for whatever his preaching might lack. What a message of cheer and hope it brings, a message that we need now more than ever before!

It Came Upon the Midnight Clear

A FEW moments before everything was peaceful upon this hillside. The shepherds were resting on their cloaks, the sheep were huddled together asleep within the enclosure, while the dog was on guard. Suddenly there is a bright light overhead. The shepherds start up, shading their eyes from its brilliance. The frightened sheep do not know which way to run, while the dog cowers close to his master.

Then the shepherds have their wonderful vision. They can hardly believe their eyes. In the sky overhead is the angel of the Lord, and they hear a voice telling them of Jesus' birth.

Bernhard Plockhorst

Apparition to the Shepherds

The angel is pointing to a spot just a short distance away, where the little town of Bethlehem is hidden among the trees. Right above it the brilliant star is shining.

All at once it seems as if the whole sky becomes lighted, and they hear that great message, "Glory to God in the highest, and on earth peace, good will toward men."

The colors of the original painting are particularly beautiful; Plockhorst among the modern German artists is noted as a colorist. His many religious pictures express lofty thoughts with great truthfulness. Their sweetness and simplicity of expression have made them great favorites, especially with children.

O Little Town of Bethlehem

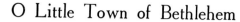

PHILLIPS BROOKS, 1868   LEWIS H. REDNER, 1868

1. O lit - tle town of Beth - le - hem, How still we see thee lie!
2. For Christ is born of Ma - ry, And gath - ered all a - bove,
3. How si - lent - ly, how si - lent - ly The Won - drous Gift is given!
4. O ho - ly Child of Beth - le - hem, De - scend to us, we pray;

A - bove thy deep and dream - less sleep The si - lent stars go by;
While mor - tals sleep, the an - gels keep Their watch of won - d'ring love.
So God im - parts to hu - man hearts The bless - ings of His heaven.
Cast out our sin, and en - ter in; Be born in us to - day.

Yet in thy dark streets shin - eth The ev - er - last - ing Light;
O morn - ing stars, to - geth - er Pro - claim the ho - ly birth,
No ear may hear His com - ing, But in this world of sin,
We hear the Christ - mas an - gels The great glad ti - dings tell;

The hopes and fears of all the years Are met in thee to - night.
And prais - es sing to God the King, And peace to men on earth!
Where meek souls will re - ceive Him, still The dear Christ en - ters in.
O come to us, a - bide with us, Our Lord Em - man - u - el!   A - MEN.

PHILLIPS BROOKS, who wrote this hymn, was a Boston preacher, and people came from all over the world to hear him, for he had such a joyful message, and made Christ seem so real. He was very fond of children, and in his home always had a supply of dolls and toys for his little friends.

Once he visited the Holy Land, and on Christmas Eve went to Bethlehem, to the spot where Jesus was born. Hour after hour he stayed there, thinking of the wonderful night of Jesus' birth. When he returned to America he wrote a Christmas carol for his Sunday-school, using the thoughts that he had had while at Bethlehem. Mr. Redner, the church organist, wrote the music, which so perfectly suits the words. Many people who never have heard the great preacher are joyfully singing, "O Little Town of Bethlehem."

The story is told that the morning after Phillips Brooks' death a mother said to her little girl, "Bishop Brooks has gone to heaven." "O Mother," the child replied, "how happy the angels will be!"

O Little Town of Bethlehem

The Wise Men on Their Way to Bethlehem

Henry A. Harper

THESE are the three Wise Men who have come a long distance, following the star, in search of the Christ Child. They have traveled over desert and mountain just to see the Baby Jesus, and to offer their gifts. Can their journey be reaching its end? They are eagerly watching the star which seems to stop just over the hill where Bethlehem lies.

We can almost imagine ourselves traveling with the Wise Men, the scene is so real. The artist spent years in studying the Holy Land, and has given his best in the picture. At one side we see shepherds watching their flocks. Can they be the same ones who heard the angel voices some nights before? One of them seems to have left the group around the fire at the call of the strangers, and is apparently pointing the way to Bethlehem.

What a wonderful winter night this is! We can almost feel the clear cold air with all its crispness. The brilliant star illuminates the whole scene. The distant hills are indistinct in a soft haze, but the deep shadows cast by the Wise Men show what a marvelous light is shining full upon them.

I Heard the Bells

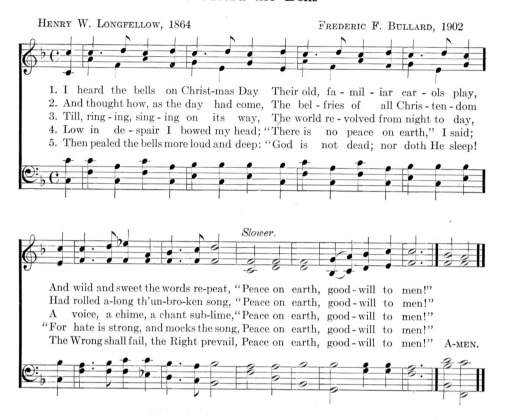

HENRY W. LONGFELLOW, 1864   FREDERIC F. BULLARD, 1902

1. I heard the bells on Christ-mas Day   Their old, fa-mil-iar car-ols play,
2. And thought how, as the day   had come, The bel-fries of   all Chris-ten-dom
3. Till, ring-ing, sing-ing on   its   way, The world re-volved from night to day,
4. Low in   de-spair I bowed my head; "There is   no peace on earth," I said;
5. Then pealed the bells more loud and deep: "God is   not dead; nor doth He sleep!

Slower.

And wild and sweet the words re-peat, "Peace on   earth,   good-will to   men!"
Had rolled a-long th'un-bro-ken song, "Peace on   earth,   good-will to   men!"
A   voice, a chime, a chant sub-lime, "Peace on   earth,   good-will to   men!"
"For   hate is strong, and mocks the song, Peace on   earth,   good-will to   men!"
The Wrong shall fail, the Right prevail, Peace on   earth,   good-will to   men!"   A-MEN.

WE are fortunate in having this hymn by Henry W. Longfellow, the most beloved, if not the greatest of American poets. Though much of his poetry is of a religious nature, very little has been set to music and can be classed among our hymns. The poet's brother, Samuel, has written a number of hymns and, as might be expected, the work of the two has sometimes been confused.

In the Longfellow home in Cambridge the study is kept very nearly as the poet left it. Visitors enter by one of the "three doors left unguarded," where the three daughters used to rush in upon him at the close of day. Besides the many gifts from the Indians of the Hia-watha legends, and from Evangeline's country, there is a chair made from the "spreading chestnut tree," under which the "village smithy" stood. As the visitor passes out, the old clock on the stairs ticks a farewell, "Forever,-Never,-Never,-Forever."

Longfellow has been called the Universal Poet, for he has written poems for everyone—children, students, workpeople, and older men and women. At one time there were people from all over the world on board a ship which was delayed for several days. To pass away the time, there was a poetry contest. It was found that Longfellow was the only poet some of whose works everyone knew.

The music for this hymn is especially appropriate. The bass particularly sounds like the ringing and singing of a bell. The last four measures are from an old and very beautiful "Amen."

I Heard the Bells

Christmas Bells   Edwin H. Blashfield

URELY this is a joyful message that the bells and the angels are giving us. Even the doves seem to wish to be included as they hover around the bell tower. Two of the angels are ringing the chimes, while the third is seated on the beam of the large lower bell. We can almost hear the rich tones of the big bells, and the angel voices, as they sing to us of the Saviour's birth.

The gargoyle in the lower corner seems strangely out of place. We do not know why such queer little creatures were ever placed on the outside of churches, unless it was to show that everything that is not beautiful and good must stay outside. This one looks as if the Christmas message were making him feel rather uncomfortable and he would like to move away. But his ugliness only serves to make the contrast all the greater, and emphasizes the beauty of the angels and the chimes.

Blashfield, the artist, is one of our own American painters. He has decorated the walls of the Congressional Library and of other public buildings.

Jesus Christ Is Risen Today

Latin, 14th Century

LYRA DAVIDICA, 1708

1. Je - sus Christ is risen to - day, Al - - - le - lu - ia!
2. Hymns of praise then let us sing, Al - - - le - lu - ia!
3. But the pains which he en - dured, Al - - - le - lu - ia!

Our tri - um - phant ho - ly day, Al - - - le - lu - ia!
Un - to Christ our heav'n - ly King, Al - - - le - lu - ia!
Our sal - va - tion have pro - cured, Al - - - le - lu - ia!

Who did once up - on the cross, Al - - - le - lu - ia!
Who en - dured the cross and grave, Al - - - le - lu - ia!
Now a - bove the sky He's King, Al - - - le - lu - ia!

Suf - fer to re - deem our loss, Al - - le - lu - ia!
Sin - ners to re - deem and save, Al - - le - lu - ia!
Where the an - gels ev - er sing Al - - le - lu - ia! A-MEN.

THIS is our most beloved Easter hymn. The swelling "Alleluias" give it a distinction all its own, and are such a spontaneous expression of our joy that we cannot help but love it. Strange to say, the authorship of this noted hymn is a mystery. It is undoubtedly a translation of an old Latin hymn, and first appeared in a little volume called *Lyra Davidica*, or Songs of David, which is now in the British Museum.

The music also puzzles us, for we do not know where it came from either. Some people think the great musician Handel wrote it, and it certainly resembles his work. But others think it was written by Worgan and his name is generally associated with it.

In spite of the fact, however, that we do not know who wrote it, or who translated it, or who composed the music, it remains our most popular Easter carol.

Jesus Christ Is Risen Today

ASTER day has always been the great day of the Christian Church. The sorrow of the past is forgotten as we think of the Risen Jesus.

This picture comes to us from the far North. It seems strange that so beautiful a painting should be in such a remote part of the world. It is from an altarpiece in the little wooden church in Molde, a fishing village in Norway, near the Arctic Circle.

The painting itself glows with color: the vivid garments of the women and the dark background of the cave serve to bring out in striking relief the white-clad angel with glorious golden hair. Like nearly all other artists, Ender has painted the features of the people with whom he is associated, and we find in these women and in the angel a decided Norwegian expression.

Alex. Ender

Holy Women at the Tomb

The women, Mary Magdalene, Mary the mother of Jesus, and Salome, are sorrowing together, when suddenly they enter the tomb to find Jesus gone and the angel vision there! Salome, in the entrance, has not yet seen the angel, but the faces of the others express amazement and wonder. Mary Magdalene starts back half afraid, putting her hand to her throat, as if to make sure that she is not dreaming. Jesus' mother, beside her, though fearfully grasping her hand, bends forward to hear every word of the message, "He is not here: for He is risen!"

No wonder the Norwegian artist chose to paint the story of the Resurrection! After the long dark winter of the Northland the springtime is especially welcome and Easter brings a double message of joy.

The Day of Resurrection

John of Damascus, C. 749
Translated by JOHN M. NEALE, 1853

HENRY SMART, 1836

1. The day of res-ur-rec-tion! Earth, tell it out a-broad;
2. Our hearts be pure from e-.il, That we may see a-right
3. Now let the heav'ns be joy-ful, Let earth her song be-gin,

The pass-o-ver of glad-ness, The pass-o-ver of God.
The Lord in rays e-ter-nal Of res-ur-rec-tion light,
Let the round world keep tri-umph And all that is there-in;

From death to life e-ter-nal, From this world to the sky,
And, list-'ning to His ac-cents, May hear, so calm and plain,
In-vis-i-ble and vis-i-ble, Their notes let all things blend;

Our Christ hath brought us o-ver With hymns of vic-to-ry.
His own "All hail!" and, hear-ing, May raise the vic-tor strain.
For Christ the Lord hath ris-en— Our Joy that hath no end. A-MEN.

FOR hundreds of years this hymn has been sung by the Greek Church. It was written by John of Damascus, a monk who lived over a thousand years ago in a monastery on the side of a hill near Jerusalem. To the Greek Church Easter Day is a most joyful occasion and is attended by great ceremony. Rev. John M. Neale, who has translated this hymn and has studied the customs of the Greek Church, describes how it was sung:

As midnight approached, the archbishop, with his priests, accompanied by the king and queen, left the church and stood on a platform outside. Crowds of people gathered around in breathless expectation, holding unlighted tapers. The priests murmured a melancholy chant, till suddenly the report of a cannon announced that twelve o'clock had struck and Easter Day had begun. Then the archbishop raised his cross, exclaiming, "Christ is Risen!"

Immediately the joyful cry was taken up by the whole mass of people and they burst forth into singing: while at the same time the darkness was driven away by the light from thousands of lighted tapers.

The Day of Resurrection

Adolphe William Bouguereau
Women at the Sepulcher

E can imagine the surprise of these women, as they came sadly to the tomb of Jesus, to find that the great stone placed before the door had been rolled away. What had happened? They hardly dare go any nearer, and yet their love for their Master makes them want to do all that they can for Him.

Hesitatingly they go a little closer, but they stop as they see a brilliant light within. Two of them drop upon their knees, while the other puts out her hand to feel the doorway, to make sure that she is not dreaming. Within is the beautiful angel, who tells them to sorrow no more, for Christ is no longer in the tomb.

The famous French artist, Bouguereau, painted this picture. When a boy it was intended that he should become a business man but, as he showed talent for painting, his father finally consented. However, he had no money to help him, so Bouguereau worked, and earned his own way, winning one prize after another, no one ever helping him. As an artist he is noted particularly for the earnest expression he gives to the eyes.

My Country, 'Tis of Thee

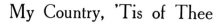

SAMUEL F. SMITH, 1832   HENRY CAREY, 1740

1. My coun - try, 'tis of thee, Sweet land of lib - er - ty,
2. My na - tive coun - try, thee, Land of the no - ble, free,
3. Let mu - sic swell the breeze, And ring from all the trees
4. Our fa - thers' God, to Thee, Au - thor of lib - er - ty,

Of thee I sing; Land where my fa - thers died, Land of the
Thy name I love; I love thy rocks and rills, Thy woods and
Sweet free - dom's song; Let mor - tal tongues a - wake; Let all that
To Thee we sing; Long may our land be bright With free - dom's

pil - grims' pride, From ev - 'ry moun - tain side Let free - dom ring!
tem - pled hills; My heart with rap - ture thrills Like that a - bove.
breathe par - take; Let rocks their si - lence break, The sound pro - long.
ho - ly light; Pro - tect us by Thy might, Great God, our King. A - MEN.

ONE day, while Samuel F. Smith was a theological student, his friend, Lowell Mason, asked him to look over a collection of tunes to see if any could be used for the Boston school children. Smith came across the melody above, but did not know that the same tune had been used as the British National Anthem since the days of George II. Thinking that it had a patriotic air, he felt an impulse to write a hymn of his own, and "America" was the result.

He turned the words over to Lowell Mason and thought no more of them till he heard them sung on the following Fourth of July at a children's celebration in Park Street Church. Soon it was sung in the public schools and at patriotic gatherings from Maine to Texas. We are glad that it has the same music as the National Anthem of the Mother Country, for it shows the bond between us.

Samuel F. Smith was a member of the famous class at Harvard to which Oliver Wendell Holmes belonged, and at the Thirtieth Anniversary Dr. Holmes wrote the following lines about him:

> And there's a nice little youngster of excellent pith,
> Fate tried to conceal him by naming him Smith;
> But he shouted a song for the Brave and the Free—
> Just read on his medal, "My country of thee!"

48

My Country, 'Tis of Thee

THIS magnificent statue, so familiar to us all, has come to stand for the Spirit of America. It was given to us by the French people in honor of the one hundredth anniversary of the Declaration of Independence, and it shows the undying friendship between the citizens of the two great countries. General Lafayette was one of the chief persons responsible for this friendship, and it is interesting to note that there is a statue of him in Paris erected by American school children. This Statue of Liberty is the loftiest in the world. Three hundred feet it towers above the waters of New York Harbor.

In 1870, when the famous sculptor, Bartholdi, was visiting America, he felt that we needed something to welcome all newcomers to this country, something to remind them of freedom and opportunity. And he conceived the idea of an enormous statue of a woman holding on high a torch, symbolizing "Liberty enlightening the world."

The French people, poor as well as rich, approved the plan, and raised the money for such a statue. But how could it be erected? It was too huge to be carved from a single

Bartholdi

Statue of Liberty, New York Harbor

piece of stone, and if put together from smaller blocks would crumble in the salt air. If it were made of solid bronze, it would be too expensive. Finally it was decided to make the statue from three hundred copper plates, which could be fitted together piece by piece and fastened to an iron framework. Care had to be taken to allow for the plates to expand in the intense heat of the sun, and to prevent electricity from forming by the contact of copper and bronze. Inside the statue are stairways leading to the head and even to the torch! Electric lights have been placed in the torch and in the pointed diadem.

It has been placed on an enormous pedestal, given by the American people, upon Bedloe's Island, where all boats must pass in entering New York harbor. To all Americans returning home it is indeed a welcome sight. And to those who are first coming to this country it stands for freedom, justice, and hope. It has inspired Jacob Riis and many others with the idea of the splendid opportunity before them here in America, and they have become among our finest citizens.

O Beautiful for Spacious Skies

KATHERINE LEE BATES, 1893, revised 1910   SAMUEL A. WARD, 1882

1. O beau - ti - ful for spa - cious skies, For am - ber waves of grain,
2. O beau - ti - ful for pil - grim feet, Whose stern, im-pas-sioned stress
3. O beau - ti - ful for he - roes proved In lib - er - at - ing strife,
4. O beau - ti - ful for pa - triot dream That sees be - yond the years

For pur - ple moun-tain maj - es - ties A - bove the fruit - ed plain!
A thor - ough - fare for free - dom beat A - cross the wil - der - ness!
Who more than self their coun - try loved, And mer - cy more than life!
Thine al - a - bas - ter cit - ies gleam, Un-dimmed by hu - man tears!

A - mer - i - ca! A - mer - i - ca! God shed His grace on thee,
A - mer - i - ca! A - mer - i - ca! God mend thine ev - ery flaw,
A - mer - i - ca! A - mer - i - ca! May God thy gold re - fine,
A - mer - i - ca! A - mer - i - ca! God shed His grace on thee,

And crown thy good with broth - er - hood From sea to shin - ing sea!
Con - firm thy soul in self - con - trol, Thy lib - er - ty in law!
Till all suc - cess be no - ble - ness, And ev - 'ry gain di - vine!
And crown thy good with broth - er - hood From sea to shin - ing sea! A - MEN.

MORE and more this splendid hymn is being used at patriotic gatherings. It challenges the best that is in us. As our country is beautiful, that for which it stands should be beautiful as well. When Katherine Lee Bates, a professor at Wellesley College, at one time traveled across the continent, she was remarkably impressed with the beauties of our great country. She later expressed her thoughts in this great hymn. The reference to the pilgrims means not only those who came to Plymouth, but all who have crossed the ocean, or even the plains and mountains of our own land, enduring the hardships of settling a new country. The "alabaster cities" refers to the buildings of the Columbian Exposition, which were so beautiful they seemed an ideal for all our cities.

This hymn has had several beautiful settings to music. The tune "Materna" is used here, for it is the most familiar.

O Beautiful for Spacious Skies

The Yosemite Valley

From a Photograph

IN this glorious country of ours there are so many beautiful places that it is difficult to choose any one that stands out above the rest. But almost everyone will agree that there are no grander views than in the Yosemite Valley. Here there are spacious skies, purple mountains, waterfalls, and deep gorges all together.

Away in the distance, at the head of the valley, rises Half Dome, that interesting mountain which looks as though it had been cleft in two; its slope is almost perpendicular. Nearer and to the left is El Capitan, one of the largest single masses of rock in the world. It rises sheer from the valley below.

The beautiful waterfall is that of the Bridal Veil, one of the loveliest in the world. As the water comes tumbling nine hundred feet over this fall it strikes a ledge, making an unusual amount of mist. When the wind blows this mist it appears filmy and shimmering, like a veil. In the late afternoon as the sun is shining upon it wonderful rainbows appear.

Do you see the little burro? We feel sorry that he is unable to appreciate all this grandeur, and yet he can take care of himself on the steep paths and places where few people can travel.

Truly "no temple made with hands can compare with Yosemite."

I Think When I Read That Sweet Story of Old

Jemima Luke, 1841

Traditional English Melody

1. I think, when I read that sweet sto - ry of old, When
2. I wish that His hands had been placed on my head, That His
3. Yet still to His foot - stool in prayer I may go, And

Je - sus was here a - mong men, How He called lit - tle chil - dren as
arm had been thrown a - round me; And that I might have seen His kind
ask for a share in His love; And, if I now ear - nest - ly

lambs to His fold, I should like to have been with them then.
look when He said, "Let the lit - tle ones come un - to Me."
seek Him be - low, I shall see Him and hear Him a - bove.   A - men.

THIS hymn is always in great demand where there are children. Would you ever guess that it was written in a stagecoach? Jemima Thompson Luke had been visiting a school where the children had been singing a fine old melody as one of their marching songs. "What a lovely children's hymn it would make, if there were only some words for it," she thought. She looked in various books, but could find none that suited her. Some time later, as she was traveling in a stagecoach, she thought of the tune again, and taking an envelope out of her pocket, wrote these three stanzas of the hymn upon it.

When she returned home she taught it to her Sunday-school class. Her father, the superintendent of the school, heard the children singing it one day. "Where did that hymn come from?" he asked. "Jemima made it," they replied. Without saying a word to her, he sent a copy to the *Sunday School Teachers' Magazine*, where it first appeared in print. Since that time it has been sung from one end of the country to the other, and has been placed in nearly every hymnal.

I Think When I Read That Sweet Story of Old

E feel sure that this must have been one of the happiest moments of Jesus' life, when the little children crowded around Him, and climbed into His arms. How eager they are to talk to Him, for they know that He is interested in all their childish play! One little child is holding out some flowers which he would like to give to Jesus, but he is asking his mother about it first. Another little boy is sitting on the ground near Jesus' feet. Do you see the palm branch he is holding? We wonder if later on he was among the children who marched with Jesus in triumph into Jerusalem, waving palm branches and

Bernhard Plockhorst

Christ Blessing Little Children

shouting, "Hosanna; Blessed is He that cometh in the name of the Lord." We are sure that Jesus will be very glad to have the little gifts. Even the babies seem to feel drawn towards Him. The little lambs too are coming up close to drink from the well, and seem to be lingering as though they would like to stay.

But the disciples in the background are coming up also. They know how busy and tired the Master is, and think that He should not be bothered in this way. Who ever heard of a great leader spending time with children? They wished to send the little ones away, but Jesus forbade them, saying, "Of such is the Kingdom of Heaven." And it is Jesus' love for little ones, more than anything else, which has been the reason for the better care of children in Christian countries from that day until now.

O Love Divine, That Stooped To Share

OLIVER WENDELL HOLMES, 1859   HENRY W. BAKER, 1866

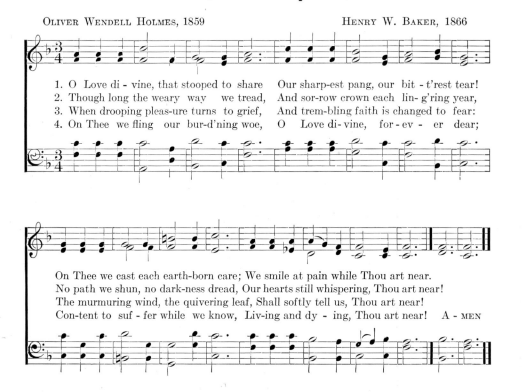

1. O Love di - vine, that stooped to share   Our sharp-est pang, our bit - t'rest tear!
2. Though long the weary way we tread,   And sor-row crown each lin- g'ring year,
3. When drooping pleas-ure turns to grief,   And trem-bling faith is changed to fear:
4. On Thee we fling our bur-d'ning woe,   O Love di- vine, for - ev - er dear;

On Thee we cast each earth-born care; We smile at pain while Thou art near.
No path we shun, no dark-ness dread, Our hearts still whispering, Thou art near!
The murmuring wind, the quivering leaf, Shall softly tell us, Thou art near!
Con-tent to suf - fer while we know, Liv-ing and dy - ing, Thou art near!   A - MEN

THE words of this hymn tell us how Jesus cared for those who were suffering. The author of this hymn was trying to do the same thing himself, for he was a physician. Probably you think of Oliver Wendell Holmes as a poet, for you have learned some of his verses in school: "Old Ironsides," perhaps, or "The Chambered Nautilus." And yet Dr. Holmes spent the greater part of his life doing the work of a doctor—his writing being incidental.

He was always very fond of hymns. He once told a friend that whenever in church there was a pause in the service, he enjoyed looking through the hymn book, covering the name of the author and trying to guess who wrote each hymn. He also said that he would be very happy if he could feel that he had left a few hymns of his own worthy of being remembered after him.

He believed that every man should have a "hobby," and that it should be as different from his regular work as possible, as it was not good for anyone to work at one thing all the time. He chose carpentering for himself, for he said that it rested his mind to be laboring with his hands. In his home he had a basement room fitted up as a workshop, and liked to boast that he was a full-fledged carpenter.

He was noted for being full of fun, and was very much in demand as a speaker. But he said of himself that while he might laugh outside, inside he was always thinking of those who were suffering and in need.

O Love Divine, That Stooped To Share

Healing the Sick

Benjamin West

WE feel very proud of Benjamin West, our first great American painter. You may know the story of his childhood, how when six years old he saw his baby sister smile in her sleep, and tried to draw it on a piece of paper. "What is thee doing, Benjamin?" his mother asked. The boy hung his head, fearing he had done wrong. His mother glanced at the paper. "Why, it is our little Sallie!" she exclaimed.

The West family were Quakers, who felt that it was wrong to devote one's time to painting pictures; yet the mother was really pleased that her son was gifted in this way, and helped him all she could. He had no paints, but the Indians near by gave him red and yellow stuff that they used on their bodies, and his mother supplied some indigo, which she used in bluing the clothes on wash day. Hair from the cat's tail served him for a brush. With this crude equipment he did so well that friends recognized his ability and sent him to Philadelphia to study. Later he went to London, where he became the Court Painter. But he always remained a true American, although he spent his last years in Europe.

The above picture was painted for some friends in Philadelphia, who were raising funds to build a hospital. In it we see Jesus coming from the Temple, surrounded by those who are beseeching Him for help. There are the lame, the blind, and both little children and older ones who are suffering we know not how. Some priests and others in the background seem to be annoyed at the disturbance, but Christ stands with His arms outstretched, and we know that He will help them all.

Break Thou the Bread of Life

MARY A. LATHBURY, 1880

WILLIAM F. SHERWIN, 1877

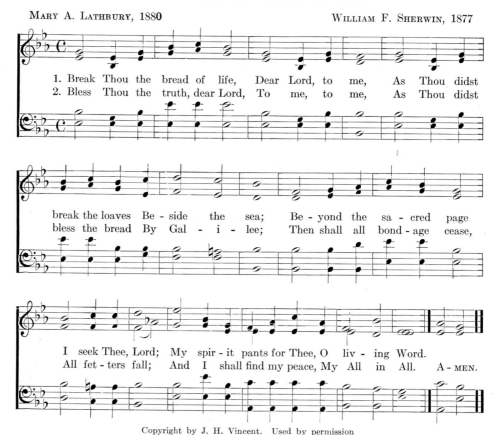

1. Break Thou the bread of life, Dear Lord, to me, As Thou didst
2. Bless Thou the truth, dear Lord, To me, to me, As Thou didst

break the loaves Be - side the sea; Be - yond the sa - cred page
bless the bread By Gal - i - lee; Then shall all bond - age cease,

I seek Thee, Lord; My spir - it pants for Thee, O liv - ing Word.
All fet - ters fall; And I shall find my peace, My All in All. A - MEN.

Copyright by J. H. Vincent. Used by permission

THIS hymn is used frequently as a communion hymn. How short it is! How simple are the words, nearly all of one syllable, and yet what a wonderful message they have! This hymn should have an added meaning when we learn that it was written to be sung by Bible students on the shore of Lake Chautauqua. We feel how appropriate are the references to the blessing of the loaves beside the Sea of Galilee.

When Mary A. Lathbury, the writer, was a young girl she showed unusual ability in writing poetry. One day she seemed to hear a voice saying to her: "Remember, my child, you have a gift for writing verse: consecrate this to me as you do your inmost spirit," and from the number of splendid hymns she has written, we can see how sincerely she answered this call.

The picture opposite was painted by the great Leonardo. We know little about his boyhood except that he was born in the little village of Vinci, near Florence, Italy. Very early he showed talent in many ways. He was a poet, musician, inventor, scientist, philosopher, and artist.

Leonardo spent two years upon this picture, a remarkably short time for so great a painting. The story is told that the prior of the monastery for which it was being painted became discouraged, for it seemed to him that Leonardo was sitting idle a great part of the time. When he spoke to him about this, however, Leonardo replied that he was not idle, but thinking. Still the prior complained to the Duke of Milan, who was paying for the picture. Whereupon Leonardo is reported to have told the prior that if he was hurried he would use him for the Judas! We know, however, that he did not do this!

56

Break Thou the Bread of Life

The Last Supper   Leonardo da Vinci

THIS is a very great and famous picture of the Last Supper. It was painted upon the dining-room wall of a convent in Milan. The picture is low and the figures but slightly larger than life-size, so that while the monks were eating it might seem as if Christ and his disciples were in the room with them.

We are fortunate, indeed, in having the picture preserved for us, for its colors soon began to fade. At one time the monastery was used as a stable, and the picture was greatly abused, a hole being cut right through it for a door! But it has been restored, giving us some idea of its original beauty.

The scene represents the moment when Jesus said, "One of you shall betray me." The words have come like a thunderbolt. It cannot be true that a traitor is among them! The party has broken into four distinct groups. Notice how the hands show the feeling of each. So expressive are they that this picture has sometimes been called "A Study of Hands."

Bartholomew—at the extreme left—staring with astonishment, has risen so quickly that his feet are still crossed. James reaches over behind Andrew to Peter, who has grasped his knife and, bending forward, whispers to John. Andrew holds up both hands in horror. Judas, with a feeling of guilt, is withdrawing from the Master, though he tries to appear unconcerned. As he grasps his money bag he has tipped over the saltcellar. John, at Jesus' side, sinks back from sheer hopelessness.

At the right, Simon, Thaddeus, and Matthew are protesting their innocence. Philip, James, and Thomas crowd to the Master, each demanding His immediate attention while saying, "Lord, Thou knowest it is not I!"

But it is Jesus Himself who attracts us most. How calmly He sits amidst so much excitement! What a wonderful face He has, so full of love and sympathy! It is said that Leonardo tried to paint the eyes looking toward us, but was not satisfied with their expression. Finally he painted them looking down, which was just the touch needed. It makes us feel that, though Christ was leader, He was one who led by serving.

In the Hour of Trial

James Montgomery, 1834   Spencer Lane, 1875

1. In the hour of tri - al, Je - sus, pray for me, Lest by base de-
2. With for-bid - den pleas - ures Would this vain world charm, Or its sor - did
3. Should Thy mercy send me Sor- row, toil, and woe; Or should pain at -

ni - al I de - part from Thee; When Thou seest me wa - ver, With a look re -
treas-ures Spread to work me harm; Bring to my re-mem-brance Sad Geth-sem-a-
tend me On my path be - low; Grant that I may nev - er Fail Thy hand to

call, Nor for fear or fa - vor Suf - fer me to fall.
ne, Or, in dark - er sem - blance, Cross-crowned Cal-va-ry.
see; Grant that I may ev - er Cast my care on Thee. A-men.

YOU cannot sing this hymn without feeling sure that the author must himself have passed through difficulties and temptations. James Montgomery was born in Scotland, the son of a minister. His parents were very anxious that he, too, should enter the ministry, so they sent him away to school for that purpose. But James was lazy, and did not get along well. Finally his teachers gave up in despair, and put him to work in a grocery store. How disappointed his parents must have been! But James did not like this any better; so, after wandering around he entered a printing office and helped publish a paper, *The Sheffield Register*. This paper seemed to bring out the best in James Montgomery. He had ability to write poems, and they were published. Also the paper was interested in such big issues as doing away with slavery, and reforming the government—subjects that made him think, and take a stand for the right. Twice he was put in prison because he wrote articles that the Government did not approve. Some of his friends urged him to flee to America, where he need not fear imprisonment, but he refused, for he loved England, and wanted to help in the reforms.

After his release he began to write hymns and sacred poems, and enter into church work. He soon had the respect of everyone—even his opponents—and the Government, as if to make up for imprisoning him, gave him a pension! Most of Montgomery's hymns have a rather sad note. Perhaps he was thinking of the time he had wasted as a boy; or, maybe, of some of the temptations as a publisher. But he surely made up in later life for former idleness. He was so beloved by the people of Sheffield that they erected a bronze statue in his honor.

In the Hour of Trial

Peter's Denial of Christ

Graf Harrach

WHY do you suppose that Peter feels so badly? He is barely able to walk, and puts out his hand to the wall for support. In the background a maid carrying a pitcher on her head is pointing at him, while the soldiers seated upon the mat are laughing and jeering.

Poor Peter, this is the hardest moment of his life! An hour before he had been in the garden with Jesus, and stood up for Him manfully. When the other disciples had fled Peter had followed at a distance, and had come into the courtyard which we see in this picture, hoping to hear some word of his Master. But when the maid points at him, and the others confront him with the question, "Did we not see thee in the garden with Him," Peter loses his courage. He is afraid that he will be arrested too. So he denies Christ, saying, "Woman, I know Him not."

But just then Jesus passes along the gallery. Although He is bound and guarded, He is not thinking of Himself, but of Peter. Jesus, with His own death looming before Him, pauses to look at Peter, though the guard shoves Him roughly along. Just then the cock in the grapevine begins to crow, and Peter remembers Jesus' words, "Before the cock crow, thou shalt deny me thrice." Peter hangs his head for shame, falters along the wall, and goes out and weeps bitterly. But this was the turning point in Peter's life. The look that Jesus gave him made him strong afterwards, so that he stood out fearlessly and boldly for Christ.

The Church's One Foundation

SAMUEL J. STONE, 1866   SAMUEL S. WESLEY, 1864

1. The Church's one foun-da-tion Is Je-sus Christ our Lord;
2. E-lect from ev-'ry na-tion, Yet one o'er all the earth,
3. 'Mid toil and trib-u-la-tion, And tu-mult of her war,
4. Yet she on earth hath un-ion With God the Three in One,

She is His new cre-a-tion By wa-ter and the Word;
Her char-ter of sal-va-tion One Lord, one faith, one birth;
She waits the con-sum-ma-tion Of peace for-ev-er-more;
And mys-tic sweet com-mun-ion With those whose rest is won;

From heav'n He came and sought her To be His ho-ly bride;
One ho-ly name she bless-es, Par-takes one ho-ly food,
Till with the vis-ion glo-rious Her long-ing eyes are blest,
O hap-py ones and ho-ly! Lord, give us grace, that we,

With His own blood He bought her, And for her life He died.
And to one hope she press-es, With ev-'ry grace en-dued.
And the great Church vic-to-rious Shall be the Church at rest.
Like them, the meek and low-ly, On high may dwell with Thee. A MEN.

WHENEVER a new church is ready for dedication, or a corner stone is to be laid, you may be fairly sure that this hymn will be sung at the service. And no finer one could be used. It makes us feel that, after all, the building is not so important, while everything depends upon what place is to be given to Jesus Christ. We feel, too, our own closeness to all other groups of Christians and that we are indeed taking our part in the great Church Universal.

This hymn emphasizes the central truths of our Faith, which are stated in the Apostles' Creed. But it also suggests to us the words of Jesus, "The stone which the builders rejected, the same is become the head of the corner."

The Church's One Foundation

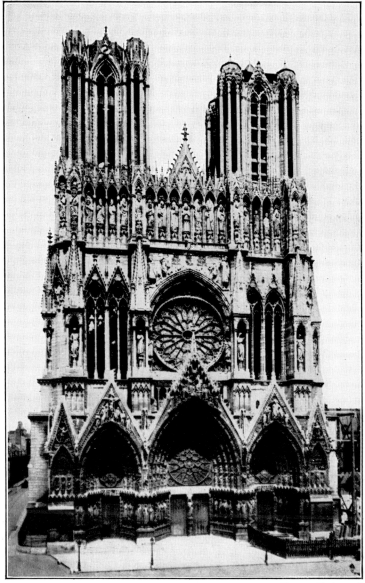

Rheims Cathedral

From a Photograph

RHEIMS CA-THEDRAL is one of the most beautiful churches in the world. Wouldn't you like to stand before the arched doorway and look up at the great church with its hundreds of statues in every niche and crevice? The two great towers appear so enormous that we can hardly believe that they do not now have their full height. At one time tall spires rose from these towers, but they were destroyed by fire in the fifteenth century. The pointed arches of the windows and doorway show that this is a true Gothic building.

We can imagine what beautiful coloring there is in the lovely rose window over the center door. Above it is the Gallery of the Kings, which contains statues of the kings of France from Clovis to Charles Seventh. Do you wonder that this place was selected for the coronation of many of the kings of France? It was to this church that Joan of Arc, the young peasant girl, escorted Charles VII to be crowned.

And yet in reality this is only a church *building*, magnificent though it may be. It is the people who love Jesus and are trying to carry on His teaching who make up the real Church. While we may love beautiful structures, a plain little wooden building is just as much God's house, if it is the place where earnest people gather to worship God and learn of His teachings.

Rheims Cathedral was badly damaged in the Great War, but the good which it has inspired cannot be destroyed.

Jesus Loves Me!

ANNA B. WARNER

WILLIAM B. BRADBURY

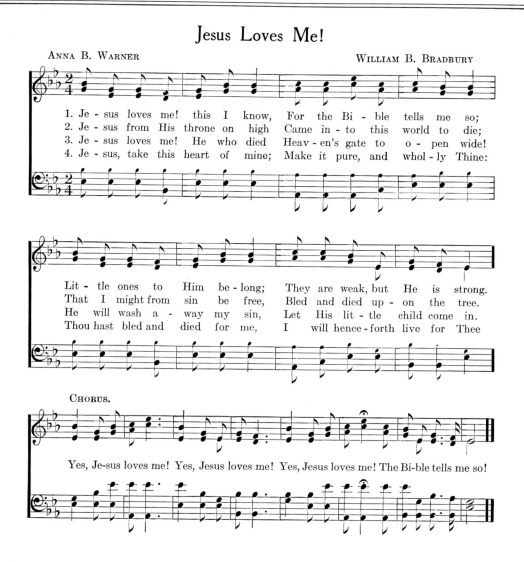

1. Je - sus loves me! this I know, For the Bi - ble tells me so;
2. Je - sus from His throne on high Came in - to this world to die;
3. Je - sus loves me! He who died Heav - en's gate to o - pen wide!
4. Je - sus, take this heart of mine; Make it pure, and whol - ly Thine:

Lit - tle ones to Him be - long; They are weak, but He is strong.
That I might from sin be free, Bled and died up - on the tree.
He will wash a - way my sin, Let His lit - tle child come in.
Thou hast bled and died for me, I will hence - forth live for Thee

CHORUS.

Yes, Je-sus loves me! Yes, Jesus loves me! Yes, Jesus loves me! The Bi-ble tells me so!

PERHAPS this was the very first hymn that you learned in Sunday-school. You will always remember it, for the words are so simple and lovely. It was written by an American woman, Anna Warner, who lived with her sister on an island in the Hudson River near West Point. These two sisters were very busy writing stories for books and magazines, and teaching Bible classes. But they will be remembered by this little hymn more than by anything else. The pretty little tune which goes so well with it has undoubtedly helped to make it popular. It was written by William B. Bradbury, who has been called the Father of Sunday-school music.

For more than half a century children all over the world have loved this hymn and known it by heart. In the foreign countries the missionaries have found that both old and young have learned it eagerly. Word has come that in the mountains of China the tribes-people are singing it in their own language. And the story is told that in India a little boy learned this hymn at a mission school, and sang it to the older men and women who were not Christians. "Who is Jesus, and what is the Bible?" they asked. Truly this hymn has brought multitudes to love Jesus. No wonder it is one of the most popular children's songs in the world!

Jesus Loves Me!

"Suffer the Little Children to Come unto Me"

Ottilie Roederstein

OULD not *you* like to come near to Jesus as these children are doing? He seems to have entered their humble home as a friend, and they are crowding eagerly around Him. How earnestly they are looking into His face! Perhaps He has been telling them a story. We know what beautiful stories He could tell, for we have some in our Bible: the Good Samaritan, the Prodigal Son, and many others. Or maybe He is asking them about themselves: what they have been learning in school, what games they like to play; or how they have been helpful at home. He may have told them of the little children of Palestine whom He had often watched at their games in the market place. The little Jewish children were very fond of playing weddings and funerals; dancing, for the weddings, and mourning, for the funerals. Perhaps Jesus played these very games Himself when He was a little boy. At any rate He must have observed them closely, for He knew just how the children played them. He noticed that children do not always agree when they are playing their games, and tells us in the Bible that sometimes older people are not so very different. In this picture see how trustingly the youngest child has placed her hand in His, as though she felt His loving interest! He surely seems to be the very best Friend the children could possibly have.

The artist, Ottilie Roederstein, is a modern German painter. While the children are dressed as European peasants, we may easily think of them as being just like ourselves.

Was There Ever Kindest Shepherd

Frederick W. Faber, 1862

Frank G. Ilsley, 1887

1. Was there ev - er kind-est shep-herd Half so gen - tle, half so sweet
2. There's a wide - ness in God's mer - cy Like the wide - ness of the sea;
3. For the love of God is broad - er Than the meas - ure of man's mind,

As the Sav - iour who would have us Come and gath - er round His feet?
There's a kind - ness in His jus - tice, Which is more than lib - er - ty;
And the heart of the E - ter - nal Is most won - der - ful - ly kind.

It is God; His love looks might - y, But is might - ier than it seems;
There is wel - come for the sin - ner, And more gra - ces for the good;
If our love were but more sim - ple, We should take Him at His word;

'Tis our Fa - ther, and His fond-ness Goes far out be-yond our dreams.
There is mer - cy with the Sav - iour, There is heal - ing in His blood:
And our lives would be all sun - shine In the sweet-ness of our Lord. A - men.

THE thought of Jesus as the Good Shepherd has appealed to many artists and hymn writers. Frederick Faber particularly loved to think of Jesus in this way, for it brought him comfort to feel that he could depend so completely on Jesus to guide him. You notice in the picture opposite that the shepherd is *leading* the sheep. He does not drive them before him. They know his voice, and follow him willingly.

Faber was an Englishman, who entered the ministry after graduating from Oxford in 1836. His life was outwardly uneventful, but he had many religious doubts and conflicts. This beautiful hymn, and many others which he wrote, show his lofty thoughts and complete trust in God.

Was There Ever Kindest Shepherd

Copyright Curtis Publishing Company, Courtesy *Ladies Home Journal*　　　William L. Taylor

The Lord Is My Shepherd

ONE of the best beloved American artists is William L. Taylor. The appealing subjects which he has chosen, his beautiful drawing, and his brilliant coloring have made his pictures favorites. Familiar poems, old songs, and passages from Shakespeare have given him ideas for many of his paintings; but the Bible has inspired his finest work, and from him we have many beautiful pictures illustrating the Psalms and the stories from the Old and New Testaments. The originals of a number of his most noted paintings decorate the walls of the building of the Curtis Publishing Company, in Philadelphia, where they are seen by thousands of visitors every year. All over the world, however, folks have had the privilege of seeing copies of Taylor's paintings, as reproduced in the Ladies' Home Journal and in smaller prints, and these have endeared him to the hearts of many.

In a letter to Walter Dower, the art editor of the *Journal*, Mrs. Taylor describes her husband's studio at Wellesley. "Minnehaha's lovely dress, Hiawatha's necklace of bear claws, David's harp, Launcelot's shield, the tiny model of a white-covered prairie schooner, Pharaoh's daughter's necklace—these and their sort help to make the old 'shop' what it is today, a shrine of remembrance."

We May Not Climb the Heavenly Steeps

John G. Whittier, 1866   William V. Wallace, 1856

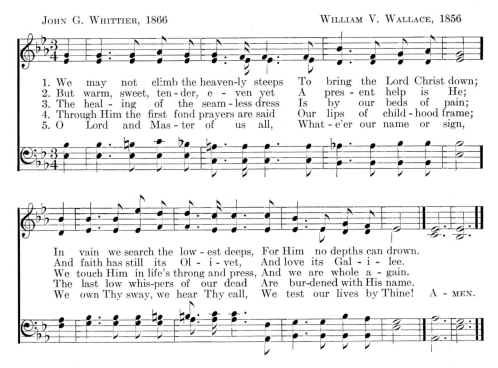

1. We may not climb the heaven-ly steeps   To bring the Lord Christ down;
2. But warm, sweet, ten-der, e-ven yet   A pres-ent help is He;
3. The heal-ing of the seam-less dress   Is by our beds of pain;
4. Through Him the first fond prayers are said   Our lips of child-hood frame;
5. O Lord and Mas-ter of us all,   What-e'er our name or sign,

In vain we search the low-est deeps, For Him no depths can drown.
And faith has still its Ol-i-vet, And love its Gal-i-lee.
We touch Him in life's throng and press, And we are whole a-gain.
The last low whis-pers of our dead Are bur-dened with His name.
We own Thy sway, we hear Thy call, We test our lives by Thine! A-men.

 SIMPLE religion was Whittier's. His childlike trust in God brought him a peace and contentment of soul which is expressed in his verses. Brought up on a New England farm, he had little of the wealth of this world, but he

> "Was rich in flowers and trees,
> Humming birds and honey bees."

Although his education was very meager, he gained

> "Knowledge never learned of schools,
> Of the wild bee's morning chase,
> Of the wild flower's time and place,
> Flight of fowl, and habitude
> Of the tenants of the wood."

Religious meetings were often held in the large old-fashioned kitchen of his father's house. On one summer day while such a meeting was taking place a large ox put his head through the open window and listened attentively while a sweet-voiced woman was speaking, much to the enjoyment of the younger members present.

At the Congress of Religions in Chicago, where sixty-six hymns were used, nine of them were by Whittier, a larger number than by any other writer. More and more his poems are being recognized for their religious and inspirational value, and are being set to music. The hymn above, like the one entitled "Dear Lord and Father of Mankind," is a section from a longer poem. Another very beautiful poem, entitled "Worship," which shows Whittier's high ideals of living, is finding its way into many of our hymn books.

> "O brother man! fold to thy heart thy brother;
> Where pity dwells, the peace of God is there;
> To worship rightly is to love each other,
> Each smile a hymn, each kindly deed a prayer."

We May Not Climb the Heavenly Steeps

Copyright Underwood & Underwood   From a Photograph

Galilee
Looking South Across the Plain of Gennesaret

HILLS and lakes had a great appeal to Whittier, for he saw divine power in their heights and depths. He never traveled a great deal; he was content to spend his life near the place of his birth; but his heart was often in the Holy Land. The mountains and waters of New England suggested to him the Sea of Galilee with its hills, and as he felt the ever-presence of Jesus he received the inspiration to write the verses opposite.

What wonderful experiences Jesus had on the hilltops! The Sermon on the Mount stands forth as the great beacon light of history, ushering in the kingdom of the Brotherhood of Man. On Mount Hermon the glorious revelation came at the time of the Transfiguration. And we are told of the many times when Jesus "went apart into a mountain to pray," as at Olivet, to gain strength for the work before Him.

What an important part, too, the Sea of Galilee played in the life of the Master! From its shores He called His first disciples to be "fishers of men." Calmness and storm alike brought forth great messages from Christ, as He taught the crowds from the boat, or put courage into the hearts of His terrified disciples.

We like to think of Galilee today as not so different from the time when Jesus and His friends walked over its neighboring hills and along its shores. Some of the villages where He taught lie buried; others are in ruins. Signs of modern civilization are creeping in, but the hills and the lake are still much the same as when the Master looked upon them.

Ride On, Ride On in Majesty!

HENRY H. MILMAN, 1827　　　　　　　　　　　　　　　JOHN B. DYKES, 1862

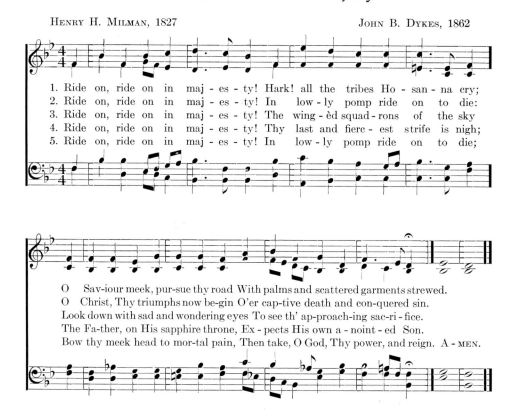

1. Ride on, ride on in maj-es-ty! Hark! all the tribes Ho-san-na cry;
2. Ride on, ride on in maj-es-ty! In low-ly pomp ride on to die:
3. Ride on, ride on in maj-es-ty! The wing-èd squad-rons of the sky
4. Ride on, ride on in maj-es-ty! Thy last and fierc-est strife is nigh;
5. Ride on, ride on in maj-es-ty! In low-ly pomp ride on to die;

O Sav-iour meek, pur-sue thy road With palms and scattered garments strewed.
O Christ, Thy triumphs now be-gin O'er cap-tive death and con-quered sin.
Look down with sad and wondering eyes To see th' ap-proach-ing sac-ri-fice.
The Fa-ther, on His sapphire throne, Ex-pects His own a-noint-ed Son.
Bow thy meek head to mor-tal pain, Then take, O God, Thy power, and reign. A-MEN.

THERE is no more beautiful hymn for Palm Sunday than this one. As we sing it we almost feel that we are among the throng following Jesus on that wonderful day.

Henry Hart Milman, the writer, was a brilliant student at Oxford University. After graduating he entered the ministry, and spent much time in studying and writing. A work called "The History of the Jews" brought him considerable distinction. Later his power as a preacher was recognized and he was made Dean of Saint Paul's Cathedral, London. This magnificent church, built by Sir Christopher Wren, is visited every year by thousands of travelers. It contains a fine copy of "Christ, the Light of the World," by Holman Hunt.

Milman wrote thirteen hymns, all of which are widely used. Most of them were for special occasions, such as Lent, Advent, Easter, and Holy Week. One of his best hymns is "For Those at Sea."

The music for the hymn given above is in German chorale form, and comes from an old hymnal compiled about two hundred and fifty years ago, called the "Hamburger Musical-isches Handbuch."

Ride On, Ride On, in Majesty!

Bernhard Plockhorst

Christ Entering Jerusalem

PLOCKHORST has given us a very beautiful idea of that great day when Jesus entered Jerusalem as the Messiah. Riding on a humble animal, Christ is coming as the Prince of Peace. How different from the Roman triumphs with their spoils of war and their captives in the train! Here there is no thought of personal glory, for Jesus' look is steadfastly ahead, towards the Temple, His Father's House. The doves flying overhead add to the peacefulness of the scene as well as suggest the ones which Jesus was to set at liberty the following day when he rebuked the money-changers, saying, "My Father's House shall be called a House of Prayer."

Jesus is surrounded by His disciples, who are rejoicing in this day. We cannot distinguish all of them, but feel sure that the young man in the lead must be John, and one of the older men following close behind Jesus must be Peter. The rest of the group are joyful pilgrims on their way to the Temple. As Jesus came by they gathered branches from the palm trees which grew by the roadside. How happy the children are as they scatter the early spring flowers in the pathway! It was the custom for pilgrims to sing as they went to Jerusalem for the Feast of the Passover, and now we hear the words of the One Hundred and Eighteenth Psalm:

"Hosanna, . . . Blessed is He that cometh in the name of the Lord"! Never did these words have so true a meaning before.

At the right we see two figures who alone seem out of sympathy with this happiness. It is such as they that caused Jesus to say, "If these shall hold their peace the stones will cry out." Jesus' kingdom of righteousness and peace must come, hard as the road ahead toward it may be.

Faith of Our Fathers, Living Still

FREDERICK W. FABER, 1849   Arranged from F. MENDELSSOHN

1. Faith of our fa - thers, liv - ing still In spite of dun - geon,
2. Faith of our fa - thers, we will strive To win all na - tions
3. Faith of our fa - thers, we will love Both friend and foe in

fire and sword, O how our hearts beat high with joy
un - to thee; And through the truth that comes from God
all our strife, And preach thee, too, as love knows how,

REFRAIN.

When - e'er we hear that glo - rious word!
Man - kind shall then in - deed be free.
By kind - ly words and vir - tuous life.
Faith of our fa - thers,

ho - ly faith, We will be true to thee till death. A - MEN.

HOW many of us would go to church next Sunday if we knew that we would be imprisoned for going? It seems almost impossible for us to imagine. It is so easy for us to go to church, that we are tempted to forget what others have gone through that we may have our Faith. But this hymn tells us very vividly of the hardships and persecution through which they went. Frederick W. Faber, the writer, had good reason to think about these things, for he came from the Huguenots of France. At one time there were seventy thousand of them who stood the test of being willing to suffer and die for their Faith. We feel sure that Faber had these times in mind when he wrote this hymn.

The music is by the famous Felix Mendelssohn. Unlike many other musicians, Mendelssohn led a very happy life. His very name, "Felix," means happy. He came from a very fine home where the parents did everything possible to bring out the best in their children. Although they were a family of means, every morning Felix and his sister Fanny had to get up at five o'clock to study and practice. How they used to enjoy Sunday morning, when they could stay in bed later! Mendelssohn's happy disposition is shown in most of his music. He was noted for writing beautiful melodies.

Faith of Our Fathers

Bayes

Departure of the "Mayflower"

WHEN the "Mayflower" was ready to set sail for England came the supreme test of the faith of the Pilgrim Fathers. They had passed through a most severe winter. They had suffered from cold and hunger. There had been sickness, and over half their number had died. Now here was a chance to return to England, where they had comfortable homes, plenty to eat, and where other members of their families were living. It must have been a great temptation to return. Then they remembered those who had died in this country; who had given their lives that we might have freedom to worship God. They must carry on their work! This country was their home. Not one soul went back.

In the picture we see the little group after they have waved their last farewell to the ship which brought them safely across the ocean. The tall man in the center of the group must, we are sure, be Elder Brewster. He has probably just offered a word of prayer, for several are still on their knees. Can it be Miles Standish in the distance, on the side of the hill, with the gun over his shoulder? The beautiful girl seated facing us we feel sure must be Priscilla. And where is John Alden? Is he seated beside her, or is he one of the youths walking by the shore?

For just a moment did the Pilgrims stand thus, thinking of the ones across the sea. Then the voice of duty called them to the making of their homes in the new land.

How Firm a Foundation

RIPPON'S Selection, 1787   WADE'S Cantus Diversi, 1751

1. How firm a foun-da-tion, ye saints of the Lord, Is laid for your
2. "Fear not, I am with thee, O be not dis-mayed; For I am thy
3. "When thro' the deep wa-ters I call thee to go, The riv-ers of
4. "The soul that on Je-sus hath leaned for re-pose, I will not, I

faith in His ex-cel-lent Word! What more can He say than to
God, I will still give thee aid: I'll strength-en thee, help thee, and
sor-row shall not o-ver-flow; For I will be near thee, thy
will not de-sert to his foes; That soul tho' all hell should en-

you He hath said, To you who for ref-uge to Je-sus have fled?
cause thee to stand, Up-held by My right-eous, om-nip-o-tent hand,
trou-bles to bless, And sanc-ti-fy to thee thy deep-est dis-tress,
deav-or to shake, I'll nev-er, no, nev-er, no, nev-er for-sake,

To you who for ref-uge to Je-sus have fled?
Up-held by my right-eous, om-nip-o-tent hand.
And sanc-ti-fy to thee thy deep-est dis-tress.
I'll nev-er, no, nev-er, no, nev-er for-sake!" A-MEN.

THIS is a great hymn about the Bible. It shows us what a source of strength we can find in God's Word. Think how many famous persons have been brought up with the Bible as their main teacher. Lincoln, as a boy, had three books: the *Bible*, *Pilgrim's Progress*, and *Aesop's Fables*. Who can say how much of his greatness was due to his early training in the Bible?

This has been the favorite hymn of many great men. General Robert E. Lee was often heard humming this tune to himself. It was also a favorite with Theodore Roosevelt; and we all know what a firm faith he had and what a great Bible student he was. The author of the hymn is unknown, except that his name began with "K."

72

How Firm a Foundation

The Puritan
Augustus Saint Gaudens

WONDER how many of us would carry our Bibles to church and Sunday-school, if they were as large as that of Deacon Chapin. Perhaps you have seen an old-fashioned Family Bible, and thought how hard it must be to use such a large book. But we all know how much our forefathers used and depended upon their Bibles, and what a help they found in God's Word, giving them the determination to overcome all hardships in founding this new country of ours.

This impressive statue by Saint Gaudens represents Deacon Chapin, the Puritan. The deacon came over with the early settlers to Boston, but soon set out with his wife and children on the perilous journey through the wilderness to Springfield, where he helped in the founding of the town.

For years he was deacon in the church, taking the place of the minister when there was a vacancy. He was also active in the town government. As we see him walking along with a firm step and determined look we feel sure that he has a worth-while purpose in view, and that the Bible which he carries takes a foremost place in his life.

Augustus Saint Gaudens, who made this statue, is one of our greatest American sculptors. Though born in Ireland, he came to New York city when six months old. As most of his work has been done in this country, we feel that we have a right to call him an American. His statues are to be found in many of our most beautiful public parks.

Who Is on the Lord's Side?

FRANCES R. HAVERGAL, 1877

Arranged by JOHN GOSS, 1871

1. Who is on the Lord's side? Who will serve the King? Who will be His help - ers
2. Not for weight of glo - ry, Not for crown and palm, En - ter we the ar - my,
3. Je - sus, Thou hast bought us, Not with gold or gem, But with Thine own life-blood,
4. Fierce may be the con - flict, Strong may be the foe, But the King's own ar - my

Oth - er lives to bring? Who will leave the world's side? Who will face the foe?
Raise the war-rior psalm; But for Love that claim- eth Lives for whom He died:
For thy di - a - dem: With Thy bless-ing fill - ing Each who comes to Thee,
None can o - ver - throw: Round His stand-ard rang-ing, Vic-t'ry to se - cure;

Who is on the Lord's side? Who for Him will go? By Thy call of mer - cy,
He whom Je - sus nam-eth Must be on His side. By Thy love con-strain - ing,
Thou hast made us will-ing, Thou hast made us free. By Thy grand re - demp-tion,
For His truth un-chang-ing Makes the tri-umph sure. Joy - ful-ly en - list - ing

By Thy grace di-vine, We are on the Lord's side; Sav-iour, we are Thine. A-MEN.

THIS magnificent hymn was written by Frances Ridley Havergal, perhaps the greatest woman hymn writer. She was a very beautiful and gifted woman, and, though she was never strong, she was able to accomplish a great deal during her lifetime. Her whole life was spent in trying to bring people to Christ. Wherever she went she tried to make sure that there was no one whom she met who did not know and love Jesus.

A good many of our best hymns have come from her pen. She never sat down and deliberately tried to write a hymn, but waited till she had an inspiration and then, wherever she was, she would jot it down on paper. At one time she was watching some children playing in a schoolyard. Suddenly the words of a hymn flashed into her mind and leaning against the wall she scratched them down.

The hymn above may not be quite so well known as some of her others, but it is full of strength and beauty. The tune is a splendid old Scotch melody, which just seems to have been made for the words.

Who Is On the Lord's Side?

Victory, O Lord!

Sir John E. Millais

ENER-ALLY we think of the leader of an army as being at the front fighting with his men. But here Moses is at a distance on a hilltop watching the battle on the plain below. The rod of the Lord is in his hand, and when the Israelites see Moses holding up the staff they feel the power of God within them, and they conquer their enemies. But when Moses puts down his arms the enemy is victorious.

So Moses stood with his arms held high till he could endure it no longer. Still he would not give in. Aaron, his brother, and Hur, who were with Moses, placed a stone upon which he might sit, and each helped him hold up an arm. We can see what a struggle Moses is having: he is fighting harder than anyone in the plain beneath. How his arms must ache! If only he could rest them for just a moment! But no! He will keep them up until the sun goes down and the battle is won.

Millais is one of the most popular artists that England has ever produced. He should never be confused with the French Millet. For, though their names are pronounced the same, their paintings are of very different subjects.

Millais did not have to struggle as many other artists; his life was very fortunate. He was handsome, rich, and talented. He was very popular as a portrait painter; and many famous people, including Gladstone, Carlyle, and Tennyson, had their portraits painted by him. He also made many historical and scriptural paintings.

Jesus Calls Us, O'er the Tumult

CECIL F. ALEXANDER, 1852   WILLIAM H. JUDE, 1887

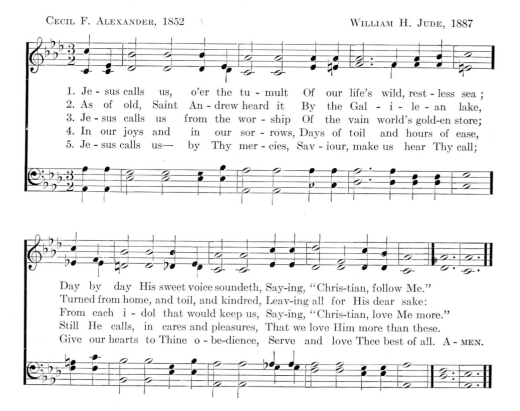

1. Je - sus calls us,   o'er the tu - mult Of our life's wild, rest - less sea ;
2. As of old, Saint An - drew heard it By the Gal - i - le - an lake,
3. Je - sus calls us from the wor - ship Of the vain world's gold-en store;
4. In our joys and   in our sor - rows, Days of toil and hours of ease,
5. Je - sus calls us— by Thy mer - cies, Sav - iour, make us hear Thy call;

Day by day His sweet voice soundeth, Say-ing, "Chris-tian, follow Me."
Turned from home, and toil, and kindred, Leav-ing all for His dear sake:
From each i - dol that would keep us, Say-ing, "Chris-tian, love Me more."
Still He calls, in cares and pleasures, That we love Him more than these.
Give our hearts to Thine o - be-dience, Serve and love Thee best of all. A - MEN.

THIS hymn is becoming more and more popular as a Conference hymn where there is a challenge to people to consecrate their lives to the service of the Master. The Brotherhood of St. Andrew has adopted it, and sometimes it is sung by thousands of men together at their meetings. The second stanza, which is occasionally omitted, is included here, as it tells such a fine story. Andrew was the very first disciple of Jesus, and he not only came himself, but brought his brother, Peter.

Would you ever guess that this hymn, sung by so many groups of men, was written by a woman? It is the same Mrs. Alexander who wrote "Once in Royal David's City," and another hymn which you probably know, "There is a Green Hill Far Away." Her hymns were written mostly for little children, but many of them are loved by older people too. Altogether she wrote about four hundred hymns.

Mrs. Alexander never cared for praise. Sometimes her friends would tell her how very famous people had spoken appreciatively of her poems, but she would pay no attention. One time, however, she was told that a man who had led a sinful life, upon hearing one of her hymns, had repented. "Thank God," she exclaimed, "I do like to hear that!"

Jesus Calls Us, O'er the Tumult

Christ and the Fishermen

Ernst K. G. Zimmermann

JESUS has been walking beside the Sea of Galilee and has come across this group of fishermen mending their nets. What strong-looking men they are! The sun and wind have tanned their faces and their muscles have been strengthened by hard work. We may well imagine that the older man has weathered many a tempest, for storms were of frequent occurrence on the Sea of Galilee. In the distance we catch a glimpse of the lake and other fishermen.

These men are talking earnestly, and it is easy to see how interested they are in what Jesus is saying. Has He been telling them about the gospel of love which He has come to proclaim? Is He asking them to follow Him and become fishers of men? The two younger men seem to approve and are eager for more. But the older man, in the foreground, has his doubts. It is hard for him to change his ideas. But how tenderly and patiently Jesus is pleading with him! He takes his hand that he may feel His friendship. We feel sure that Jesus will not go on until He has cleared up all the difficulties in the mind and heart of the old fisherman.

He Leadeth Me: Oh, Blessed Thought!

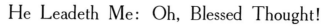

JOSEPH H. GILMORE, 1859　　　　　　　　WILLIAM H. BRADBURY, 1864

1. He lead-eth me: Oh, bless-ed thought! Oh, words with heavenly com-fort fraught!
2. Sometimes 'mid scenes of deep-est gloom, Sometimes where Eden's bow-ers bloom,
3. Lord, I would clasp Thy hand in mine, Nor ev-er mur-mur nor re-pine;
4. And when my task on earth is done; When, by Thy grace, the vic-t'ry's won;

What-e'er I do, wher-e'er I be, Still 'tis God's hand that lead-eth me.
By wa-ters calm, o'er trou-bled sea— Still 'tis His hand that lead-eth me.
Con-tent, what-ev-er lot I see, Since 'tis my God that lead-eth me.
E'en death's cold wave I will not flee, Since God thro' Jor-dan lead-eth me.

REFRAIN.

He lead-eth me, He lead-eth me, By His own hand He lead-eth me:

His faith-ful fol-lower I would be, For by His hand He lead-eth me. A-MEN.

THIS hymn, like so many others, was produced in a very few moments. Mr. Gilmore had been giving a talk on the Twenty-third Psalm, at a midweek service. The idea that impressed him most in connection with it was that God was leading us and what a blessed thing this leadership was! At the close of the meeting he went to the house of some friends, and while they were conversing, he took a pencil from his pocket and wrote the stanzas and refrain on a piece of paper which he happened to have with him.

He handed it to his wife, and thought no more about it. But Mrs. Gilmore sent it to a religious paper, where it was published as a poem. Three years later, as Mr. Gilmore went into a church, he picked up a hymn book, which he opened at random. Imagine his surprise when he turned to "He Leadeth Me," among the hymns! Mr. Bradbury had seen the verses and composed the music which is so well suited to it.

When the author wrote this hymn he was still quite a young man. From the useful life which he later lived as minister, as college professor, and writer, we feel sure that he himself trusted in the leadership of his Lord of which the hymn tells so well.

He Leadeth Me: Oh, Blessed Thought!

William Hilton

Peter Freed by the Angel

WERE you ever in a strange place where you did not know your way? If so, how glad you were to have someone come and lead you back to familiar sights again!

In this picture we see Peter in prison, where he had been placed for preaching about Jesus. He was lying in his cell asleep, bound between two soldiers, when suddenly a light appeared, and an angel took him by the hand and led him forth from the prison. It seems almost impossible for him to pass these men without wakening them. Do you see the heavy iron door with its bolts and chains? We can hardly imagine how the soldiers could still continue asleep.

Peter himself can hardly believe his own eyes but thinks that he must be dreaming as he passes the soldiers and goes out through the great iron gate into the street again. How grateful he must have felt that God had led him safely out of danger!

O Jesus, Thou Art Standing

William Walsham How, 1867

Justin H. Knecht, 1799
Edward Husband, 1871

1. O Je - sus, thou art stand - ing Out - side the fast - closed door,
2. O Je - sus, thou art knock - ing; And lo! that hand is scarred,
3. O Je - sus, thou art plead - ing In ac - cents meek and low,

In low - ly pa - tience wait - ing To pass the thresh - old o'er:
And thorns Thy brow en - cir - cle, And tears Thy face have marred:
"I died for you, my chil - dren, And will ye treat me so?"

We bear the name of Chris - tians, His name and sign we bear.
Oh, love that pass - eth knowl - edge, So pa - tient - ly to wait!
O Lord, with shame and sor - row We o - pen now the door;

Oh, shame, thrice shame up - on us, To keep Him stand - ing there!
Oh, sin that hath no e - qual, So fast to bar the gate!
Dear Sav - iour, en - ter, en - ter, And leave us nev - er more! A - men.

IN the book of Revelation we find the words, "Behold, I stand at the door and knock." These words seem to have served as a basis for this hymn. We feel sure that the writer must have been very earnest in his efforts to bring Jesus into the hearts of his friends, and we are not surprised to find that William How, though a Bishop in the Church of England, was an active worker in the slum districts on the East Side of London. When he first began his work there people would point at him saying, "There goes a bishop." But as they came to know him better, they said, "There goes *the* Bishop." And finally, when they learned to love him for all that he did for them, they would say, "There goes *our* Bishop."

O Jesus, Thou Art Standing

William Holman Hunt

The Light of the World

IT surely seems as if this picture and this hymn were made on purpose for each other. The door, which represents the entrance to the human soul, is indeed fast closed. The high weeds before it show that it has not been opened for some time. There is not even a sign of a footprint outside. A bat is hovering in the vines overhead. Yet Jesus still hopes that the door may be opened. We can almost hear the knocking, gentle but persistent. Does the owner know who is seeking to come in?

Ruskin tells us that the white robe shows it is a Prophet, the jeweled robe and breastplate indicate a Priest, and the crown of gold a King. The crown of thorns is now bearing leaves "for the healing of the nations." Yet the crown of thorns and the scars on the hands show us that it is the same Saviour who died for us. How tenderly and patiently He is knocking! Perhaps the owner is afraid to open the door for fear of what may be outside. But if he only knew he would gladly throw it open wide; for there is a beautiful orchard spread before him, and lying right at the very door are golden apples.

This beautiful picture hangs in a chapel of Keble College, in Oxford. Beneath the picture runs this beautiful verse, "Behold, I stand at the door, and knock: If any man hear my voice, and open the door, I will come in to him, and will sup with him, and he with Me." (Rev. 3: 20.) A copy is in St. Paul's, London, where thousands of people see it every year. In this same city of London Holman Hunt, the artist, was born. He painted many religious pictures, going to Palestine to study so that his pictures might be as near the truth as possible.

Nearer, My God, to Thee

SARAH F. ADAMS, 1841

LOWELL MASON, 1856

1. Near - er, my God, to Thee, Near - er to Thee! E'en though it be a cross That rais - eth me, Still all my song shall be,
2. Though, like the wan - der - er, The sun gone down, Dark - ness be o - ver me, My rest a stone, Yet in my dreams I'd be,
3. There let the way ap - pear, Steps un - to heaven; All that Thou send - est me, In mer - cy given: An - gels to beck - on me,
4. Then, with my wak-ing thoughts Bright with Thy praise, Out of my ston - y griefs Beth - el I'll raise; So by my woes to be
5. Or, if on joy - ful wing, Cleav - ing the sky, Sun, moon, and stars for - got, Up - ward I fly, Still all my song shall be,

Near - er, my God, to Thee, Near - er, my God, to Thee, Near - er to Thee. A- MEN.

IT would be hard to find a hymn more beloved by everyone, Protestant, Catholic, and Jew. The refrain, "Nearer, My God, to Thee," is so simple that it has a universal appeal. It was written by a gifted Englishwoman, Mrs. Sarah Flower Adams, and is based on the story of Jacob. It is said that whenever travelers from Christian lands, in touring Palestine, stop at Bethel where Jacob had his dream, they always sing this hymn. It has been of great help and comfort to many people in times of crisis.

This was the favorite hymn of President McKinley, and formed the last words he was heard to utter. When the great steamship "Titanic" was sinking and panic threatened, the band played "Nearer, My God, to Thee." Many times in France this hymn was played over the graves of our American boys.

During the Civil War a gentleman was driven from his home by soldiers, and was greatly depressed. He happened to be passing a dilapidated log cabin and heard someone singing the words, "Nearer, My God, to Thee." Jumping from his horse he entered the cabin, and saw an old woman who was pitifully poor, and yet happy in singing this hymn. Ashamed of himself for being discouraged he mounted his horse and started on with renewed faith and energy.

Nearer, My God, to Thee

Jacob's Dream   Murillo

WOULD not you like to have a beautiful dream like this and see angels passing up and down a ladder? At the foot lies Jacob, with only a stone under his head for a pillow. Yet he felt that God was near him.

Have you ever heard of the Stone of Scone? It is supposed to be this very stone upon which Jacob placed his head. After having been taken to Egypt, to Ireland, and to Scone, in Scotland, it was placed under the Coronation Chair in Westminster Abbey, London, where it still remains.

What lovely faces the angels have! Murillo, the artist, was a Spanish painter. Instead of painting the Court ladies and gentlemen, he loved to paint the little beggar children of the streets. Some of his most famous pictures are of them at their play; and he often used them as models for his angels.

Murillo had been a poor boy himself. His parents died before he was eleven years old, and he had to earn his own living. He secured work at helping a painter: cleaning brushes, mixing paint, and running errands. But this very work gave him an opportunity to try his own skill, and he was soon able to make a living, painting banners, and making portraits of persons on the street, which he would finish quickly while the crowd watched. When he had saved a little money, he walked nearly all the way to Madrid to study with the famous teacher, Velasquez. After three years he returned home and started painting.

He was very devout, and painted mostly religious subjects. Swearing and ill conduct were forbidden in his studio. He always kept his friendship with the poorest beggars, even though the most prominent men in the city were proud to know him. He was so generous that it was said he gave away to the poor nearly all that he earned.

Love Divine, All Love Excelling

Charles Wesley, 1747

John Zundel, 1870

1. Love Di - vine, all love ex - cell - ing, Joy of heaven to earth come down!
2. Breathe, O breathe Thy lov - ing Spir - it In - to ev - ery troub - led breast!
3. Come, Al - might - y, to de - liv - er, Let us all Thy life re - ceive!
4. Fin - ish, then, Thy new cre - a - tion; Pure and spot - less may we be:

Fix in us Thy hum - ble dwell - ing, All Thy faith - ful mer - cies crown.
Let us all in Thee in - her - it, Let us find Thy prom - ised rest.
Sud - den - ly re - turn, and nev - er, Nev - er more Thy tem - ples leave!
Let us see Thy great sal - va - tion—Per - fect - ly re - stored in Thee;

Je - sus, Thou art all com - pas - sion, Pure, un - bound - ed love Thou art;
Take a - way the love of sin - ning; Al - pha and O - me - ga be;
Thee we would be al - ways bless - ing, Serve Thee as Thy hosts a - bove,
Changed from glo - ry in - to glo - ry, Till in heaven we take our place,

Vis - it us with Thy sal - va - tion, En - ter ev - ery trembling heart.
End of faith, as its be - gin - ning, Set our hearts at lib - er - ty.
Pray, and praise Thee with - out ceas - ing, Glo - ry in Thy per - fect love.
Till we cast our crowns be - fore Thee, Lost in won - der, love, and praise. A - men.

THE names of Charles and John Wesley are famous throughout the Christian Church. They believed in preaching not only in church, but on street corners to the masses who never entered a church building. Though people threw stones at them, still they kept on. So strict were they in their manner of living that they were called "Methodists." Besides preaching, Charles wrote over six thousand hymns. He always kept a notebook with him and jotted down some of his hymns on horseback, and some even in bed!

You may imagine it was quite a problem for their father, a minister, to feed and clothe his nineteen children. One day a member of the House of Parliament wanted to adopt Charles. He would live in a fine house, have fine clothes and all he wanted. But Charles preferred the love and companionship of his parents, even with hardships, to a life of greater ease away from them. What splendid parents they must have been to have inspired such a feeling! Perhaps from them came to him, first of all, the idea of the Love Divine.

Love Divine, All Love Excelling

Martin von Molitor

The Prodigal Son and His Father

THE only way we can think of divine love is by comparing it with human love. And what more beautiful example is there of human love than that of the Prodigal Son and his father? You know the story, one of the greatest stories in the world. The younger son asked for his share of his father's fortune and went away to a far country where he spent it most foolishly.

Then one day his money was gone, and his friends who were glad enough to enjoy his gifts disappeared also. The boy was forced to seek work and, to keep himself from starving, took care of some swine. Sometimes he was so hungry that he would eat almost anything, even the husks he fed to the swine.

Then he began to think of his father. He knew he had done wrong, and was ashamed to go home. Yet he knew his father loved him in spite of everything that had happened. If only he could take the place of a servant in his father's home it would be better than being away!

And we know how his father received him when he returned. His love for his boy was so great that he forgave all his sins and took him back home once more. In the picture we see how the boy, dressed in the swineherd's garb, has flung himself on his knees before his father. His hands are clasped in deep repentance. But the father gently raises him and takes him in his arms.

Dear Lord and Father of Mankind

JOHN G. WHITTIER, 1872   FREDERICK C. MAKER, 1887

1. Dear Lord and Fa - ther of man - kind, For - give our fev - 'rish ways;
2. In sim - ple trust like theirs who heard, Be - side the Syr - ian sea,
3. O Sab - bath rest by Gal - i - lee! O calm of hills a - bove!
4. Drop Thy still dews of qui - et - ness, Till all our striv - ings cease;
5. Breathe through the heats of our de - sire Thy cool - ness and Thy balm;

Re - clothe us in our right - ful mind; In pur - er lives Thy
The gra - cious call - ing of the Lord, Let us, like them, with -
Where Je - sus knelt to share with thee The si - lence of e -
Take from our souls the strain and stress, And let our or - dered
Let sense be dumb; let flesh re - tire; Speak through the earth-quake,

ser - vice find, In deep - er rev - 'rence, praise.
out a word, Rise up and fol - low Thee.
ter - ni - ty, In - ter - pret - ed by love.
lives con - fess The beau - ty of Thy peace.
wind, and fire, O Still Small Voice of calm!   A - MEN.

E are very glad that some of Whittier's poems are found in our hymn books, for more than any other he seems to be a poet of the people. He grew up on a New England farm where hard work left little time for reading and study. One day his sister found this verse upon his slate:

> And must I always swing the flail,
> And help to fill the milking-pail?
> I wish to go away to school;
> I do not wish to be a fool.

Determined to have more education, he worked for years in his spare time, making shoes and teaching, till when nineteen he had saved enough to go to Haverhill Academy for two seasons. Here he gained most from the use of the library, and was able to read and study later by himself.

Whittier loved the freedom of the open air. As his family were Quakers, he was taught that we should live simply, as Jesus did, and love all mankind. When there were slaves in our country, Whittier was among the first to try to have them freed. He felt that God had called him to this cause, even though he lost friends, and his life was in danger. Many of his best poems were called forth to right the evil condition found in the slave states. "Love God and serve your fellow-men" was his ideal. In the hymn above he emphasizes service by purer lives, in his quiet, but forceful way.

Dear Lord and Father of Mankind

Jesus by the Sea

Alexandre Bida

DID you ever climb to the top of a hill where you could look out over the country beneath you far away into the distance? How quiet and peaceful everything seemed, and how beautiful! I am sure that you must have felt that God was very near.

In the picture we see Jesus resting on the hillside overlooking the Sea of Galilee. How refreshing it must have been after busy days of preaching and healing! Here He could be alone and talk over with God the plans for His work.

We know that Jesus often went apart by Himself to some such quiet spot. And He always came back with renewed strength for the task before Him.

Fairest Lord Jesus

MUNSTER, 1677
Translated c. 1850

Silesian Folk Song
Arranged by RICHARD S. WILLIS, 1850

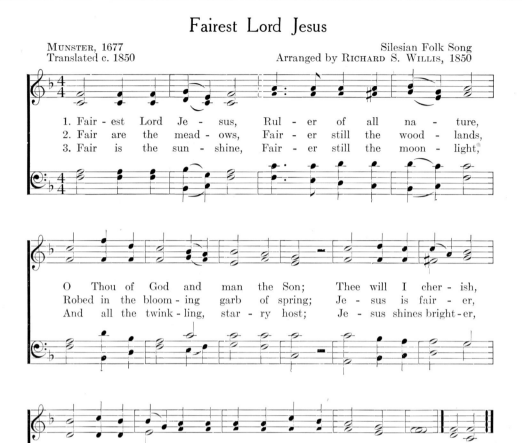

1. Fair - est Lord Je - sus, Rul - er of all na - ture,
2. Fair are the mead - ows, Fair - er still the wood - lands,
3. Fair is the sun - shine, Fair - er still the moon - light,

O Thou of God and man the Son; Thee will I cher - ish,
Robed in the bloom - ing garb of spring; Je - sus is fair - er,
And all the twink - ling, star - ry host; Je - sus shines bright - er,

Thee will I hon - or, Thou, my soul's glo - ry, joy, and crown.
Je - sus is pur - er, Who makes the woe - ful heart to sing.
Je - sus shines pur - er, Than all the an - gels heaven can boast. A-MEN.

THIS is called the Crusaders' Hymn. I am sure you have heard of the Crusades: how, long ago, the people of Europe gathered armies together to go to the Holy Land. At that time the Turks were in possession of the country, and the people of Europe felt that it was wrong for Christ's birthplace to be in the hands of those who did not believe in Him. Army after army left Europe to fight against the Turks, but they were not successful.

Then the idea came to some children in Germany that they might be the ones to win back the Holy Land. A group of them gathered together to march on foot over mountains and rivers for hundreds of miles to Palestine, where they thought that the country would be given over to them. As they marched from one town to another they sang songs about Jesus. The words above are thought to be those of one of the hymns they used. They have been set to the music of an old Silesian Folk Song.

Unfortunately, there were too many difficulties to be overcome and the little Crusaders never reached Palestine.

Fairest Lord Jesus

The Christ Child   H. Hofmann

WHAT fairer picture is there of the boy Jesus than this one? You recognize it as coming from the picture of "Christ Among the Doctors." Jesus is just twelve years of age; a thoughtful boy, but one who is keenly alert and interested in all that is going on in the world around Him. We do not wonder that this is one of the most popular pictures ever painted.

Hofmann, the artist, was born in Germany. Though he is ranked as a historical and portrait painter, he is best known for his religious pictures. More of his paintings are seen in our Sunday-schools than of any other artist. They are popular because they are clear and easy to understand, and appeal to us on account of their beauty.

Holy, Holy, Holy!

REGINALD HEBER, 1827   JOHN B. DYKES, 1861

1. Ho - ly, Ho - ly, Ho - ly! Lord God Al - might - y!
2. Ho - ly, Ho - ly, Ho - ly! all the saints a - dore Thee,
3. Ho - ly, Ho - ly, Ho - ly! tho' the dark - ness hide Thee,
4. Ho - ly, Ho - ly, Ho - ly! Lord God Al - might - y!

Ear - ly in the morn - ing our song shall rise to Thee;
Cast - ing down their gold - en crowns a - round the glass - y sea;
Though the eye of sin - ful man Thy glo - ry may not see,
All Thy works shall praise Thy name, in earth, and sky, and sea;

Ho - ly, Ho - ly, Ho - ly! mer - ci - ful and might - y!
Cher - u - bim and Ser - aphim fall - ing down be - fore Thee,
On - ly Thou art Ho - ly, there is none be - side Thee,
Ho - ly, Ho - ly, Ho - ly! mer - ci - ful and might - y!

God in Three Per - sons, bless - ed Trin - i - ty!
Which wert, and art, and ev - er - more shalt be.
Per - fect in pow'r, in love, and pur - i - ty.
God in Three Per - sons, bless - ed Trin - i - ty! A - MEN.

REGINALD HEBER, who wrote the words of this hymn, has also given us "From Greenland's Icy Mountains" and "The Son of God Goes Forth to War." The words of this hymn are based on a passage from the book of Revelation, "They rest not day and night, saying, 'Holy, holy, holy, Lord God Almighty.'" This is the great hymn of the Trinity. It is stately and beautiful.

The music was written for it and is always used with it. It is called Nicæa, from a town in Asia Minor. Long ago in that town a council met to decide upon the teachings of the Church. It was found that some Christians were saying one thing about God, while others were teaching quite differently. So here they talked over just what should be taught. The most important decision which they made was called the Doctrine of the Trinity, which means that God shows Himself to us in three ways: as God the Father, and as Christ the Son, and as the Holy Spirit.

90

Holy, Holy, Holy!

Angel Heads

Reynolds

WOULDN'T you like to hear the beautiful song of praise which these angels are singing? We may well imagine that their song is: "Holy, Holy, Holy!" Did you know that these heads were all drawn from one little girl? Sir Joshua Reynolds, the artist, was very fond of painting children, and in his studio he had all sorts of toys and musical instruments, so that the little ones would not become tired as he worked on their pictures.

One day Lord Gordon brought his little daughter, Frances, to the studio. Sir Joshua was delighted; for she was such a beautiful child, with wonderful golden hair and deep blue eyes. He could not decide in just what position to paint her, so he made a number of sketches to see which he liked best. First he drew her looking straight ahead, as she watched him at work. Then he caught her expression as she looked up, and then to one side. He liked them all so well that he finally decided to use every one of them in the picture. As she looked so much like an angel, he added the wings, the clouds, and the light coming from above, and named the picture, "Angel Heads."

For the Beauty of the Earth

Folliott S. Pierpont, 1864

Arranged from Conrad Kocher, 1838

1. For the beau-ty of the earth, For the glo-ry of the skies,
2. For the won-der of each hour, Of the day and of the night,
3. For the joy of hu-man love, Bro-ther, sis-ter, par-ent, child,
4. For Thy Church that ev-er-more Lift-eth ho-ly hands a-bove,

For the love which from our birth O-ver and a-round us lies,
Hill and vale, and tree and flower, Sun and moon, and stars of light,
Friends on earth, and friends a-bove, For all gen-tle thoughts and mild,
Off-'ring up on ev-ery shore Her pure sac-ri-fice of love,

Refrain

Lord of all, to Thee we raise This our hymn of grate-ful praise. A-men.

THIS is the most widely known work of Folliott S. Pierpont, who was born in Bath, England, and attended Queen's College. He wrote this hymn originally, with several more stanzas, as a communion hymn, but it has been used extensively for Flower Services, Thanksgiving Day, and as a Children's Hymn. The refrain at the close of each stanza seems the natural expression of the joyful Christian life. Even very little children can learn to sing this refrain, while the rest of the stanza is read, or sung as a solo.

The familiar music to which this hymn is sung is called "Dix" because William Dix wrote the words, "As with gladness men of old did the guiding star behold," with which this music has been usually associated.

For the Beauty of the Earth

Courtesy of Raymond & Whitcomb Company   From a Photograph

Fujiyama

ONE of the most beautiful spots on the earth is this snow-capped mountain rising from the shores of the ocean. In the springtime, when the cherry blossoms are on the trees and the whiteness of the summit is outlined against the deep blue of the sky, the effect is truly wonderful. Probably no other mountain has been used so much in art. It is especially dear to the hearts of the Japanese people, and many pilgrimages are made to it every year.

Basho, one of the greatest and most dearly loved Japanese poets, has written,

> "Climbing this mountain pathway,
> No lovelier flower I see
> Than that shy little violet, hiding modestly."

If we but have the eyes to see it, there is beauty all around us, and there should be thankfulness for it in our hearts.

Dare to Be Brave, Dare to Be True

W. J. Rooper

Duncan Hume

1. Dare to be brave, dare to be true, Strive for the right, for the Lord is with you; Fight with sin brave - ly, fight and be strong; Christ is your Cap - tain, fear on - ly what's wrong.
2. Dare to be brave, dare to be true, God is your Fa - ther, He watch - es o'er you; He knows your tri - als; when your heart quails, Call Him to res - cue, His grace nev - er fails.
3. Dare to be brave, dare to be true, God grant you cour - age to car - ry you through; Try to help oth - ers, ev - er be kind, Let the op - pressed a strong friend in you find.

Refrain

Fight then, good sol - diers, fight and be brave; Christ is your Cap - tain, might - y to save. A - MEN.

THIS heroic hymn certainly ought to appeal particularly to every American boy. It reminds us of the Boy Scout Law, which includes in its challenge: "To be brave, loyal, helpful, friendly, obedient, and reverent." It emphasizes the qualities for which our flag stands: the red for bravery, the white for purity, the blue for truth.

Are you familiar with the ideals which were held up before the boys and girls of the Middle Ages? There were seven virtues: Faith, Hope, Charity, Prudence, Temperance, Chastity, and Fortitude. It is interesting to see how many of these are covered by the Scout Law and by this hymn.

Dare to Be Brave, Dare to Be True

David as a Good Shepherd

Madame Bouguereau

WHAT an experience David has just had! The shepherd's life is not always an easy one; for even when everything seems calm and peaceful danger is often lurking not far away.

For some reason the little lamb must have wandered away to the edge of the thicket, where the lion was hiding; for surely no shepherd would take his flock into such a rugged spot as this. When David heard the cry of distress, never thinking of his own safety he ran after the lion and slew him.

In the picture he is holding the little lamb safe in his arms, and is giving thanks to God for having given him strength to overcome the lion. The dark hills in the background bring out the strong figure of David. What a manly face he has! His whole attitude shows the courage and power which he will need later on. Here on the hills he was getting the training and strength which stood him in such good stead when he met the giant, Goliath. Here also he was learning to know God, and gaining that spiritual power which helped him to be such a true friend to Jonathan, and to be such a beloved king.

Elizabeth Gardiner was a New Hampshire girl who went to France to study under the great artist, Adolphe Bouguereau, whom she afterwards married. Madame Bouguereau's pictures have become very popular but, on account of her French name, she is often not recognized as an American.

Onward, Christian Soldiers

S. Baring-Gould, 1865   Arthur S. Sullivan, 1871

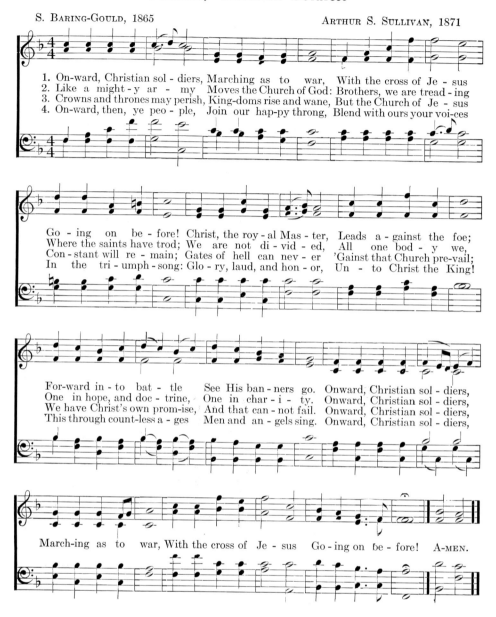

1. On-ward, Christian sol - diers, Marching as to war, With the cross of Je - sus
2. Like a might-y ar - my Moves the Church of God: Brothers, we are tread - ing
3. Crowns and thrones may perish, King-doms rise and wane, But the Church of Je - sus
4. On-ward, then, ye peo - ple, Join our hap-py throng, Blend with ours your voi-ces

Go - ing on be - fore! Christ, the roy - al Mas - ter, Leads a - gainst the foe;
Where the saints have trod; We are not di - vid - ed, All one bod - y we,
Con - stant will re - main; Gates of hell can nev - er 'Gainst that Church pre-vail;
In the tri - umph - song: Glo - ry, laud, and hon - or, Un - to Christ the King!

For-ward in - to bat - tle See His ban - ners go. Onward, Christian sol - diers,
One in hope, and doc - trine, One in char - i - ty. Onward, Christian sol - diers,
We have Christ's own prom-ise, And that can - not fail. Onward, Christian sol - diers,
This through count-less a - ges Men and an - gels sing. Onward, Christian sol - diers,

March-ing as to war, With the cross of Je - sus Go-ing on be - fore! A-men.

ONE day there was to be a union meeting of some of the Sunday-schools of Yorkshire, England, and Rev. Sabine Baring-Gould was to take his scholars several miles to join forces with a neighboring village. He dreaded the undertaking, for he knew how mischievous the boys were, and what a long walk it was. "If there was only something that they could sing as they walked," he thought, "the trip would not be half so hard." He tried to think of some hymn that would do but, as he could find none, he decided the night before to write something himself. So he went to his study, and in a short time wrote this hymn. We can well imagine how enthusiastically the children must have greeted this new hymn, and that the journey was not half so tiresome. It is one of the very best marching hymns that we have.

Onward, Christian Soldiers

THIS statue of St. George, by Donatello, is one of the finest in the world. It represents a splendid type of Christian soldier, standing for courage, service, and championship of the weak. Little is known of the life of St. George, though there are many stories of his brave deeds. The legend of his killing the dragon is the most famous.

As St. George was on his way to the Holy Land he is said to have passed through the kingdom of Libya, where the people were living in terror of a fierce monster. They shut themselves within the walls of a city, but the creature ate up their cattle and sheep which were outside, and then demanded their children! The day had come when the king's beautiful daughter was to be given to this dragon, and the people had been forced to send her forth to his den. While on her way she heard the sound of a horse's hoofs and, looking up, saw St. George upon a beautiful

St. George

Donatello

white horse. She begged him to run for his life, but when he heard her story he said, "God forbid! I will slay the dragon." Just then the monster appeared, and after a terrible combat St. George was victorious.

Returning to the city, he was greeted with shouts of praise. "Do not thank me, but God," he said. He spoke so earnestly about Jesus that all the people became Christians. They offered him gold, but he distributed it among the poor. Then he rode on to do other deeds of kindness.

He has become the patron saint of England, and to be a Knight of St. George and wear the cross is an honor which comes to only the bravest soldier or knight.

Stand Up, Stand Up for Jesus!

GEORGE DUFFIELD, JR., 1858   GEORGE J. WEBB, 1837

1. Stand up, stand up for Je - sus! Ye sol - diers of the Cross;
2. Stand up, stand up for Je - sus! The trump - et call o - bey;
3. Stand up, stand up for Je - sus! Stand in His strength a - lone;
4. Stand up, stand up for Je - sus! The strife will not be long;

Lift high His roy - al ban - ner! It must not suf - fer loss;
Forth to the might - y con - flict In this His glo - rious day.
The arm of flesh will fail you, Ye dare not trust your own:
This day the noise of bat - tle; The next, the vic - tor's song.

From vic - t'ry un - to vic - t'ry His ar - my shall He lead,
Ye that are men, now serve Him A - gainst un - num - bered foes;
Put on the gos - pel ar - mor, And watch - ing un - to pray'r,
To Him that o - ver - com - eth A crown of life shall be;

Till ev - 'ry foe is van-quished And Christ is Lord in - deed.
Let cour - age rise with dan - ger, And strength to strength op-pose.
Where du - ty calls, or dan - ger, Be nev - er want - ing there
He with the King of Glo - ry Shall reign e - ter - nal - ly. A-MEN.

WE cannot sing this hymn, I am sure, without feeling more loyal to Jesus. What spirit it has! It just seems to carry us along with it! It was inspired by a last message given by Dudley Tyng, a young minister in Philadelphia. One day as he was watching a corn-shelling machine, he met with an accident. Everything possible was done to save his life, but in vain. When asked if he had any last message for his friends, he replied: "Tell them to stand up for Jesus."

Mr. Duffield, a friend of Tyng's and himself a minister, felt that these words were too great to be lost. So he put the thought into a poem, which he read at the close of his sermon the following Sunday. It is interesting to know that shortly before his death Mr. Tyng had preached a remarkable sermon, at the invitation of the Young Men's Christian Association, upon the text, "Go now ye that are men, and serve the Lord." Dr. Duffield refers to this in his second verse. With the stirring music to which the words were set, this has become one of our best known hymns.

Stand Up, Stand Up for Jesus

Head of St. Paul

Raphael

 A Y B E you have not thought of St. Paul as a soldier before. He surely does not look like one in this picture; he seems rather to be a thinker. But he himself felt very decidedly that he was fighting for Jesus. He even tells us of the armor for Christians: "The breastplate of righteousness, feet shod with the gospel of peace, the shield of faith, the helmet of salvation, and the sword of the Spirit, which is the Word of God."

No soldier of the Cross ever endured more for Christ than St. Paul. He was the first to feel that Jesus' teachings were too wonderful to be told only to those near by. So he spent most of his life traveling to far countries and preaching about Jesus. No obstacle was great enough to turn him back. He tells in a letter some of his hardships: how he was shipwrecked, stoned, beaten, robbed, and how he fought with wild beasts. And as his work was nearing its close he felt that he had won the battle, for he wrote: "I have fought a good fight, I have finished my course, I have kept the faith!"

Many people consider Raphael the greatest of all painters. And certainly no one has ever surpassed him in representing sweetness and beauty of expression. You are probably familiar with the Sistine Madonna and the Madonna of the Chair, two of his most famous paintings. Raphael painted so beautifully that princes from many countries wished him to paint for them. Though he did not live long, so hard did he work that he has left us nearly three hundred paintings. This picture is part of a larger painting, and is the finest that we have of St. Paul.

Rescue the Perishing, Care for the Dying

Fanny J. Crosby, 1870   William H. Doane, 1870

1. Res - cue the per - ish - ing, care for the dy - ing, Snatch them in pit - y from
2. Tho' they are slighting Him, still He is wait-ing, Wait - ing the pen - i - tent
3. Down in the hu-man heart, crushed by the tempter, Feel - ings lie bur - ied that
4. Res - cue the per - ish - ing, du - ty de-mands it; Strength for thy la - bor the

sin and the grave; Weep o'er the err-ing one, lift up the fall - en,
child to re - ceive; Plead with them ear-nest-ly, plead with them gen - tly;
grace can re - store; Touched by a lov-ing hand, wak - ened by kind - ness,
Lord will pro - vide; Back to the nar-row way pa - tient - ly win them;

Refrain.

Tell them of Je - sus, the might - y to save. ⎤
He will for - give if they on - ly be - lieve. ⎟ Res - cue the per - ish - ing,
Chords that were bro - ken will vi - brate once more. ⎟
Tell the poor wan-d'rer a Sav - iour has died. ⎦

care for the dy - ing; Je - sus is mer - ci - ful, Je - sus will save. A - men.

COULD you believe that the author of this hymn was blind? When Fanny Crosby was only six weeks old, a poultice placed upon her eyes caused her to lose her sight. Hard as her blindness must have been, Fanny was always cheerful. When only eight years old she wrote this little rhyme,

> Oh, what a happy soul am I!
> Although I cannot see,
> I am resolved that in this world
> Contented I will be.

She went to a school for blind children, where she studied so hard that eventually she became one of the teachers. She was always so active that it was hard to realize that she was blind. When asked to speak at large meetings she often would go all by herself. Police-men and railroad men gladly helped her on and off the trains.

One day she visited a mission in the New York slums. In spite of her blindness she could feel the wretchedness and misery. Returning home, she wrote "Rescue the Perishing," to inspire others to do their part in helping the unfortunate people of the slums to lead better lives.

This hymn is only one of nearly eight thousand that Fanny Crosby wrote. What a useful life she led, even though blind!

Rescue the Perishing, Care for the Dying

Christ the Consoler

Ernst K. G. Zimmermann

LTHOUGH this painting is of a home in Palestine, it is not so different from those in New York which so saddened Fanny Crosby, and led her to write the hymn. On every side is poverty: the jar with the handle gone, the cupboard with the broken door, the bare walls, and the bed of straw.

But it is the suffering boy who attracts our attention. With great effort he has turned toward Christ, as if he felt the power of His presence, and assurance that he would be well again. The grandmother, beside the boy, is not so easily affected. She has lived long and has known the world. She has become accustomed to its hardships, and is resigned to the worst.

But the mother, with the boy's head in her lap, is going to hope as long as there is a spark of life left in her son. We wonder if it was she who had gone into the street to bring Jesus into the home, or if He had simply felt the need, and had come Himself.

How tenderly Jesus is bending forward! The light from His figure is shining full upon the boy, who, we can feel sure, is gaining strength every minute.

Bringing In the Sheaves

KNOWLES SHAW

GEORGE A. MINOR

1. Sow-ing in the morn-ing, sow-ing seeds of kind-ness, Sow-ing in the noon-tide
2. Sow-ing in the sun-shine, sow-ing in the shad-ows, Fear-ing nei-ther clouds nor
3. Go-ing forth with weep-ing, sow-ing for the Mas-ter, Tho' the loss sus-tained our

and the dew-y eve; Wait-ing for the har-vest, and the time of reap-ing,
win-ter's chill-ing breeze; By and by the har-vest, and the la-bor end-ed,
spir-it oft-en grieves; When our weep-ing's o-ver, He will bid us wel-come,

We shall come, re-joic-ing, Bring-ing in the sheaves.

CHORUS

Bring-ing in the sheaves. Bring-ing in the sheaves,
Bring-ing in the sheaves, We shall come, re-joic-ing, Bring-ing in the sheaves,
Bringing in the sheaves, Bringing in the sheaves, We shall come, rejoicing, Bringing in the sheaves.

THIS popular harvest hymn is a general favorite. The repetition, both in the words and the music, makes it easy to learn and to remember, and both of these features make it specially useful for out-of-door services.

The words of the hymn are based on the passage found in the One hundred and twenty-sixth psalm:

"They that sow in tears shall reap in joy.

"He that goeth forth and weepeth, bearing precious seed,

"Shall doubtless come again with rejoicing, bringing his sheaves with him."

Bringing in the Sheaves

Copyright Taber Prang Art Company

The Gleaners

Jean François Millet

HOW hard these women are working at their task in the field! The reapers have gone by, and in the distance we see them tying the wheat into bundles and loading it upon wagons. But, as some of the wheat has escaped, these women are eagerly gathering all that remains. Into their aprons they are putting the broken heads, while they carry the longer sheaves in their hands. To bend over as they are doing would be very tiresome for us, but they do not seem to mind, for they are so intent upon their work. The man on horseback in the distance is the overseer of the field. He has probably sent the women to this place to gather the stalks so that nothing will be wasted.

Far in the background stand a number of buildings with their thatched roofs. These are probably barns, and perhaps also the homes of some of the peasants. How glad they must be to return to them when the day's work is over, and they can rest from their labors!

One of these women is probably younger than the others. Do you notice how she has thrown her arm over her back so that she will not become stooped with her toil? She also has a border from her cap, covering her neck, to prevent sunburn. As is so often the case in Millet's paintings, we see very little of the faces of the peasants. It is their work which is important, and they are doing it thoroughly. We cannot help admiring the cheerful and uncomplaining way in which these women are keeping at their task, however humble it may seem.

I Would Be True

HOWARD ARNOLD WALTER

JOSEPH YATES PEEK

1. I would be true, for there are those who trust me;
2. I would be friend of all— the foe, the friend - less;

I would be pure, for there are those who care; I would be
I would be giv - ing, and for - get the gift; I would be

strong, for there is much to suf - fer; I would be brave, for
hum - ble, for I know my weak - ness; I would look up, and

there is much to dare, I would be brave, for there is much to dare.
laugh, and love, and lift, I would look up, and laugh, and love, and lift. A-MEN.

Used by permission of J. Yates Peek

AS has been the case with many others, this hymn was written without a thought of publication. Howard Walter was in Japan when he wrote it as a poem, which he called "My Creed," a personal challenge to himself. He had graduated from Princeton College and Hartford Theological Seminary, in both of which institutions he had distinguished himself as a scholar. As he felt the need of Christian work in foreign countries, he spent the year after graduation, at Waseda University, Tokio, working under the Young Men's Christian Association. He was very fond of the Japanese students, and made many warm friends among them. He often went hiking with them over the mountains, or on boat rides to the neighboring islands.

It was during this year in Japan that he wrote "My Creed." One day a line or two occurred to him from something which his mother had written him, and sitting down at his desk he completed the whole poem in some fifteen minutes .

Walter gave his life in work on the foreign field, serving in India and China, as well as in Japan. Although he did not live long, he accomplished much. "My Creed," which has been so beautifully set to music, holds forth a high standard of ideals for the youth of today, and is a favorite hymn in gatherings of young people.

I Would Be True

WHAT a glorious road of opportunity lies before this young girl as she starts forth on her life-work! Her *Alma Mater*, as a college mother, has been teaching and caring for her, but now the time has come for the girl to leave this protecting love and start out for herself. The tender fingers upon the shoulder of the maiden show how the mother yearns to keep her daughter longer; and yet, as duty calls, she wants her to go forth. With the book in her hand and the lamp to guide her, the girl is starting out prepared for a life of service. We feel sure that she will be true to the best that is in her, for "there are those who care."

This beautiful Memorial was given by Dr. Palmer to Wellesley College in honor of his wife, Alice Freeman Palmer, the second president. Although one of the youngest of college presidents, Alice Freeman had such high standards and such wise plans that she made a valuable contribution to the cause of education for women. The thousands of letters which at her death her husband received from statesmen, lawyers, clerks, country wives, even from those whom the world calls outcasts, in fact from every walk of life, testified to the power of her friendship and the inspiration of her example.

This tablet may be seen in

Daniel Chester French

The Alice Freeman Palmer Memorial

the Wellesley Chapel, "in the heart of the college which she loved." It is one of the masterpieces of Daniel Chester French, among the greatest of American sculptors. French was born in New Hampshire, but studied extensively in Europe. His work shows great versatility, and in prominent places all over the United States may be found examples of the many types of sculpture which he made. They include busts of famous men and women, colossal statues of idealistic figures, bronze doors and other forms of relief. His works are characterized by a lofty intellectual quality.

O God, Our Help in Ages Past

ISAAC WATTS, 1719

WILLIAM CROFT, 1708

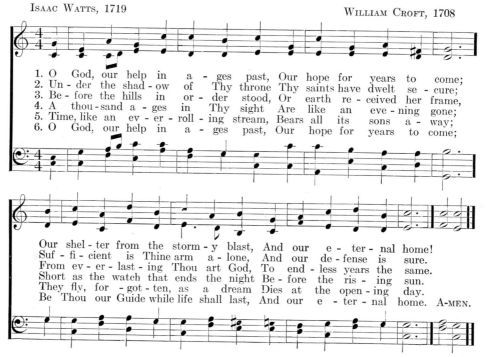

1. O God, our help in a - ges past, Our hope for years to come;
2. Un - der the shad - ow of Thy throne Thy saints have dwelt se - cure;
3. Be - fore the hills in or - der stood, Or earth re - ceived her frame,
4. A thou-sand a - ges in Thy sight Are like an eve - ning gone;
5. Time, like an ev - er - roll - ing stream, Bears all its sons a - way;
6. O God, our help in a - ges past, Our hope for years to come;

Our shel - ter from the storm - y blast, And our e - ter - nal home!
Suf - fi - cient is Thine arm a - lone, And our de - fense is sure.
From ev - er - last - ing Thou art God, To end - less years the same.
Short as the watch that ends the night Be - fore the ris - ing sun.
They fly, for - got - ten, as a dream Dies at the open - ing day.
Be Thou our Guide while life shall last, And our e - ter - nal home. A-MEN.

PERHAPS you have already noticed the name of Isaac Watts in connection with hymns. He has written many splendid hymns, and has been called the "Father of English Hymn-writers." Watts lived at a time when people were punished for their religion. When Isaac was only a baby his father was put in prison for six months for his belief. The mother often sat on the stone steps of the prison, holding the little Isaac in her arms. Every day she would come and spend hours in singing for the comfort of her husband. Probably Isaac inherited from his mother his love for music.

Watts was never strong, he was practically an invalid all his life. And yet he was as active as possible. When just a young man he objected one day to the translation of the Psalms used in his father's church. "Why don't you give us something better, young man," the elder said sternly. Watts accepted the challenge, and by evening had written a hymn which was sung at the service. This was the beginning of his hymn-writing for which he has become so famous.

This hymn is based upon the Ninetieth Psalm, and is considered one of his best. As he suffered so much himself, we are sure that he must have depended on God for his own help and strength. The music, too, well carries out the idea of the hymn, with its slow, steady rhythm and strong chords.

It is interesting that Watts, who wrote such beautiful and dignified hymns, should have written for children also. For many years his children's songs have been sung. Perhaps you know some of them. "How Doth the Little Busy Bee," and "Let Dogs Delight to Bark and Bite" are as well known as any. Also the lovely little cradle song, "Hush, My Dear, Lie Still and Slumber."

The English people have shown their love for Watts by erecting a beautiful memorial for him in Westminster Abbey. It represents him as seated at a table writing, while angels whisper songs in his ears.

O God, Our Help in Ages Past

Briton Riviere

Daniel's Answer to the King

F ANYONE ever needed God's help it was Daniel when he was among the lions. Yet how calm and fearless he seems! We feel sure by his determined face that he cannot easily be turned aside from what he believes to be right.

When only a boy Daniel was taken captive to Babylon, yet he never forgot the God of his own people. You remember how he ate simple food and grew so strong and wise that he became one of the chief advisers of the king. But some jealous nobles planned to have him put out of the way. As they knew he prayed by his window every day, they urged the king to pass a decree that the king alone should be worshiped for thirty days, any offender to be thrown to the lions. But Daniel prayed as usual to God. Then the king saw how foolish he had been, but he could not change a law upon which he had placed his seal.

Daniel was not afraid even among the lions, for he knew he had done right. How strange the lions must have felt! Never before had such a person been among them. In a remarkable way the artist has caught the restlessness of the lions in this new situation. Though Daniel has turned his back upon them in answering the call of the king, and though one of the lions is ready to spring, they seem restrained by some unseen power.

The King of Love My Shepherd Is

Henry W. Baker, 1868   John B. Dykes, 1868

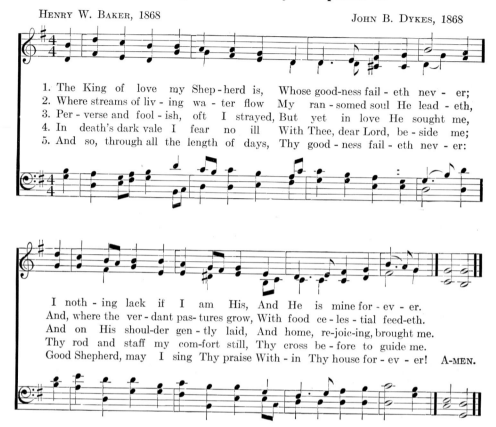

1. The King of love my Shep-herd is, Whose good-ness fail - eth nev - er;
2. Where streams of liv - ing wa - ter flow My ran - somed soul He lead - eth,
3. Per - verse and fool - ish, oft I strayed, But yet in love He sought me,
4. In death's dark vale I fear no ill With Thee, dear Lord, be - side me;
5. And so, through all the length of days, Thy good - ness fail - eth nev - er:

I noth - ing lack if I am His, And He is mine for - ev - er.
And, where the ver - dant pas - tures grow, With food ce - les - tial feed-eth.
And on His shoul-der gen - tly laid, And home, re-joic-ing, brought me.
Thy rod and staff my com-fort still, Thy cross be - fore to guide me.
Good Shepherd, may I sing Thy praise With - in Thy house for - ev - er! A-men.

OF course you have noticed how very similar this hymn is to the Twenty-third Psalm, the first psalm probably that you learned by heart. At one time the singing of the Psalms was practically the only music that we had in our churches, and even now many of our best hymns are based upon the Psalms—many perhaps that we would not think of at first as coming from a psalm.

Anyone who was interested in writing a hymn like this we feel sure must have had a very simple and sincere faith himself. Would you ever dream that it was written by a baronet who was very wealthy and lived in a beautiful castle? In spite of all his riches and fame, however, he put Jesus Christ first and spent much of his time in Christian service. He has written a number of very fine hymns. The last words he spoke were the last two lines of this beautiful hymn:

"Good Shepherd, may I sing Thy praise
Within Thy house forever!"

The King of Love My Shepherd Is

The Lost Sheep

Alfred U. Soord

 OW different is this picture from most others of the Good Shepherd! So often we see a peaceful scene with a little lamb in the shepherd's arms, and yet the real test of a shepherd's love is what he is willing to endure when the sheep, perverse and foolish, have gone astray.

How far this sheep must have wandered! It almost makes us tremble when we think of the dangers here. What a wild place this mountainside is! Night is rapidly coming on and a storm is approaching. Added to this, eagles are hovering above, watching their chance when they can attack. It seems as if nothing can save the poor sheep. Its strength is almost gone.

Then it hears the shepherd's voice. He has been willing to risk his life to follow after. The thorns have torn his skin and the sharp rocks have cut him, but still he has kept on, not thinking of himself. How grateful the sheep must have been to be gently laid upon the strong shoulders of the shepherd and brought home amidst rejoicing!

A Mighty Fortress Is Our God

MARTIN LUTHER, 1529

MARTIN LUTHER, 1529

1. A might-y fort-ress is our God, A bul-wark nev-er fail - ing:
2. Did we in our own strength con-fide, Our striv-ing would be los - ing;
3. And though this world, with dev - ils filled, Should threat-en to un - do us;
4. That Word a - bove all earth-ly powers—No thanks to them—a-bid - eth;

Our help - er He, a - mid the flood Of mor - tal ills pre - vail - ing.
Were not the right man on our side, The man of God's own choos - ing.
We will not fear, for God hath willed His truth to tri - umph through us.
The Spir - it and the gifts are ours Thro' Him who with us sid - eth.

For still our an-cient foe Doth seek to work us woe; His craft and power are
Dost ask who that may be? Christ Je - sus, it is He; Lord Sab - a - oth His
The prince of dark-ness grim—We trem - ble not for him; His rage we can en -
Let goods and kin-dred go, This mor - tal life al - so; The bod - y they may

great, And armed with cru-el hate, On earth is not his e - qual.
name, From age to age the same, And He must win the bat - tle.
dure, For lo! his doom is sure—One lit - tle word shall fell him.
kill: God's truth a - bid - eth still, His king-dom is for - ev - er. A-MEN.

P ROBABLY this hymn has played a more important part in the growth of the Christian Church than any other, for it enabled Luther to spread his teaching and start the Reformation. Even his enemies said: "The whole people are singing themselves into his doctrine."

When Luther lived the Church felt that the Bible should not be read by ordinary people, and all hymns were sung in Latin. But Luther thought that Christians should understand what was being said in church, so he translated the Bible into the language of the common people, and also wrote hymns for them to sing in their own tongue. The Church authorities were very angry and ordered his death. But the common people followed him and sang his hymns at work, at play, on the street, and even on the battlefields. It gave them courage and strength for whatever might be before them.

The words of this hymn are based on the Forty-sixth Psalm, "God is our refuge and strength." The music was also written by Luther. Upon his monument at Wittenburg are inscribed the words in German:

"A mighty fortress is our God."

A Mighty Fortress Is Our God

Wartburg Castle

From a Photograph

 OESN'T this castle look like the ones you read about in story-books? What a magnificent outlook it has from the top of the steep hill! From the watchtower you can see for miles over a plain on one side and a forest on the other.

It is thought that Luther had this castle in mind when he wrote his great hymn. When his enemies were planning to put him to death, his friends rushed him to this stronghold and hid him securely. How glad he must have been to have had the protection of these strong walls! Here his enemies could not harm him. God seemed to him like this great fortress.

But, also, while he was here he had a struggle with himself. Temptation came to him in various forms. At one time he is said to have hurled an inkstand at the vision of his Tempter. The very blot is supposed to have been on the wall until recently, when tourists chipped it off for souvenirs. A hole is now in the wall in place of the famous blot. It may well have been that Luther had also in mind that God is our strong protection against the evil thoughts that arise within ourselves.

What a Friend We Have in Jesus

JOSEPH SCRIVEN

CHARLES C. CONVERSE

Moderato

1. What a Friend we have in Je - sus, All our sins and griefs to bear!
2. Have we tri - als and temp - ta - tions? Is there trou-ble a - ny-where?
3. Are we weak and heav - y - la - den, Cum-bered with a load of care?

What a priv - i - lege to car - ry Ev - 'ry-thing to God in pray'r!
We should nev - er be dis - cour-aged; Take it to the Lord in pray'r.
Pre - cious Sav-iour, still our Ref - uge— Take it to the Lord in pray'r.

Oh, what peace we of - ten for - feit! Oh, what needless pain we bear!
Can we find a friend so faith - ful, Who will all our sor-rows share?
Do thy friends despise, for - sake thee? Take it to the Lord in pray'r;

All be-cause we do not car - ry Ev - 'ry-thing to God in pray'r.
Je - sus knows our ev-'ry weak-ness; Take it to the Lord in pray'r.
In His arms He'll take and shield thee; Thou wilt find a sol - ace there. A-MEN.

JOSEPH SCRIVEN, who wrote this hymn, tried like Jesus to be a friend to everyone in need. A college graduate, and comparatively well off, he did not hesitate to do the hardest kind of work if there was need. One day he was seen on the street, dressed as a working man, carrying a saw.

"There goes an honest-looking man," someone said, "I will ask him to saw some wood for me." "He won't saw wood for *you!*" exclaimed someone else. "That is Joseph Scriven, and he saws wood only for poor widows and sick people! *You* are able to pay!"

He led a very quiet, helpful life. Few persons knew that he could write poetry. One day a friend found the words of this hymn, and asked him about them. "They were written to comfort my mother at one time," he replied, "I never intended anyone else to see them."

But we are glad he was willing they should be published, that others should gain comfort and help from them too.

What a Friend We Have in Jesus

H. Hofmann

At the Home of Mary and Martha

HOW we wish that we might have talked with Jesus as did Mary and Martha! We know that He often visited their home in Bethany. It was just a short distance from Jerusalem, but the Mount of Olives shut it off from the city, making it a peaceful spot in which to rest. When He was very tired from preaching and healing, it must have been a great comfort to be able to come to this home. In the picture we can see what a lovely home it was. We can almost feel the cool breezes from the mountainside coming in at the open window.

Martha is busy preparing the meal. She wishes their Guest to have the very best that their home can give. But Mary is sitting at His feet, listening to every word that He says. Jesus felt that Mary had chosen the better part. He would prefer to have a simpler meal, with more time to talk with His friends. Perhaps Mary has been asking about some problems that have been troubling her, or how she can help Him in the great work that He has come to do. Just these same questions we have now, and Jesus wants us still to feel that we can turn to Him at any time with them.

Jesus, Lover of My Soul

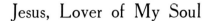

CHARLES WESLEY, 1740

S. B. MARSH, 1834

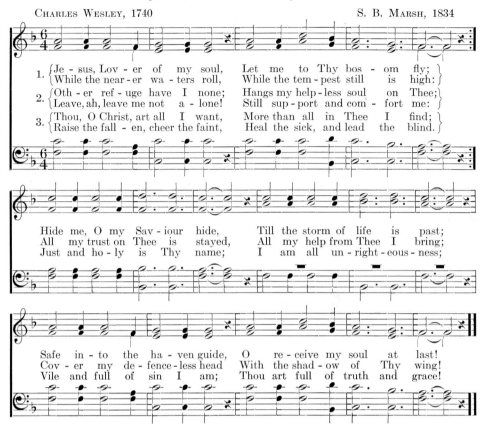

1. { Je - sus, Lov - er of my soul, Let me to Thy bos - om fly; }
{ While the near-er wa - ters roll, While the tem - pest still is high: }

2. { Oth - er ref - uge have I none; Hangs my help-less soul on Thee; }
{ Leave, ah, leave me not a - lone! Still sup - port and com - fort me: }

3. { Thou, O Christ, art all I want, More than all in Thee I find; }
{ Raise the fall - en, cheer the faint, Heal the sick, and lead the blind. }

Hide me, O my Sav - iour hide, Till the storm of life is past;
All my trust on Thee is stayed, All my help from Thee I bring;
Just and ho - ly is Thy name; I am all un - right - eous - ness;

Safe in - to the ha - ven guide, O re - ceive my soul at last!
Cov - er my de - fence-less head With the shad - ow of Thy wing!
Vile and full of sin I am; Thou art full of truth and grace!

UNDOUBTEDLY this is the favorite hymn sung upon the ocean. It is considered the greatest of Charles Wesley's hymns, although it is one of the earliest he wrote. The date given is 1740, shortly after his return to England from visiting America. This was one of the hardest times for Wesley, and he was often driven from place to place. We do not know whether the idea of the hymn came to him from a tempest on the ocean, or from storms of human passion, for he encountered both.

There are several lovely stories connected with the writing of this hymn. Some say that as Wesley was walking along the coast during a storm a sea bird flew to his breast for protection. Others tell how a dove pursued by a hawk sought safety in a similar manner.

Most of Wesley's sea hymns come from his actual experiences. We know that he often prayed in peril on the sea. In his journal, written while crossing the Atlantic, he writes:

I prayed for power to pray, for faith in Jesus Christ . . . and knew that I abode under the shadow of the Almighty. The storm was at its height. At four o'clock the ship made so much water that the captain, finding it impossible otherwise to save her from sinking, cut down the mizzen mast. In this dreadful moment, I bless God, I found comfort and hope. . . . Toward morning the sea heard and obeyed the divine voice, "Peace, be still." My first business today—may it be the first business of all my days—was to offer up the sacrifice of praise and thanksgiving.

Numberless thousands who have been in danger and temptation have found help in the use of this hymn. It has been set to several fine tunes, the one used above being one of the earliest and best known.

Jesus, Lover of My Soul

Courtesy of the Boston & Maine Railroad

Where "the Nearer Waters Roll"

From a Photograph by R. H. Newcomb

HOW glorious is the view of the waves dashing upon the rocks and sending their fine spray high into the air! The thundering of the breakers, as they pound away, and the ever changing surf, fascinate us as we gaze upon the scene. For ages these rocks have withstood the wind and the waves. But there are weaker places in them where the surf is wearing away caves, and carving fantastic figures. As the tide rushes in and out twice each day it continues this work, eroding, undermining, and constantly, but slowly, changing the form of these ledges.

The huge overhanging prominence is called "Pulpit Rock." No voice is needed to preach here, nor indeed could it be heard. The sea itself is speaking to us and telling of the great unfathomable power of the Creator.

The sea birds visit these headlands in great numbers. Here they alight as they hunt for food in the surrounding waters, or rest in safety from their enemies.

But to sailors and to voyagers upon the sea these rocks present a very different appearance. Beautiful and interesting as they may be to the poet, artist, and student, such reefs are very treacherous in time of storm. They have been the cause of so many wrecks that they are dreaded by navigators. No wonder there is a great sense of relief and thankfulness when the danger is passed and safety is found within the haven.

❧   ❧   ❧   ❧   ❧   ❧   ❧   ❧

God, the All-Merciful

(RUSSIAN HYMN)

Henry F. Chorley, 1842
John Ellerton, 1870

Alexis T. Lwoff, 1833

1. God the All-mer-ci-ful! earth hath for-sak-en Thy ways of
2. God the All-right-eous One! man hath de-fied Thee, Yet to e-
3. God the All-wise! by the fire of Thy chas-tening Earth shall to
4. So shall Thy chil-dren with thank-ful de-vo-tion Praise Him who

bless-ed-ness, slight-ed Thy word; Bid not Thy wrath in its
ter-ni-ty stand-eth Thy word; False-hood and wrong shall not
free-dom and truth be re-stored; Through the thick dark-ness Thy
saved them from per-il and sword, Sing-ing in cho-rus from

ter-rors a-wak-en: Give to us peace in our time, O Lord!
tar-ry be-side Thee: Give to us peace in our time, O Lord!
king-dom is has-tening: Thou wilt give peace in Thy time, O Lord!
o-cean to o-cean, Peace to the na-tions and praise to the Lord. A-men.

THIS hymn is one of the great challenges for Peace. The original words, written by Henry Chorley, were somewhat different. But John Ellerton, a number of years later, seeing the possibilities of the hymn, revised it in its present form.

Ellerton was born in London, in a refined religious home. During his boyhood the great teachings of the Bible were familiar topics of conversation. As a young man he entered the ministry, and most of his life was spent in small churches. But Ellerton was not limited by his surroundings. Hymns became his specialty: the study of hymns, the editing of hymn books, but particularly hymn writing. When we sing "Saviour, again to Thy dear name we raise," and the Easter hymn, "Welcome, happy morning; age to age shall say," we can think of them as coming from his pen.

The music to which these words are set is that of the Russian National Anthem. Born in Reval, Alexis Lwoff began at home his education in music. In 1836 he succeeded his father as Director of the Imperial Court Chapel. Lwoff showed talent in many lines, being an accomplished violinist, as well as a writer of several operas and of considerable church music. The hymn above with its rich harmonies and strong rhythm is, however, the work which makes his memory live.

God the All-Merciful

Signal of Peace

Cyrus Dallin

AS a friend this Indian messenger is coming toward us, desiring Peace. He and his race have suffered much at the hands of others. But now he advances with the uplifted signal, and the unspoken prayer to the All-Powerful, "Give to us Peace in our time."

The Indian and his horse seem to be one, so closely have they been associated for many years. So completely have the horse and the Indian adapted themselves to each other, it seems almost impossible to believe that before the white man came there were no horses in America.

Cyrus Dallin, the artist, is one of our foremost American sculptors, being noted particularly for depicting Indian life. Born in the West, Mr. Dallin lived for some time among the Blackfoot Indians. There he studied the manner of life of those groups which were least affected by civilization. His understanding of the Indian is shown in all his works, especially in the well-known statue, "The Appeal to the Great Spirit," which is in front of the Boston Museum of Fine Arts. The Indian, seated upon his horse, has stretched forth his hands, and with face turned toward the heavens is uttering a prayer for his race.

This "Signal of Peace" received a gold medal at the Chicago Exposition in 1893, and now stands in Lincoln Park in that city. Besides his portrayals of Indian life Mr. Dallin has made statues of many famous persons, examples of his work being found in the Congressional Library at Washington, and in many of the larger cities of America.

From Greenland's Icy Mountains

REGINALD HEBER, 1819   LOWELL MASON, 1823

1. From Green - land's i - cy moun - tains, From In - dia's cor - al strand,
2. What tho' the spic - y breez - es Blow soft o'er Cey - lon's isle;
3. Shall we, whose souls are light - ed With wis - dom from on high;
4. Waft, waft, ye winds, His sto - ry, And you, ye wa - ters, roll,

Where Af - ric's sun - ny foun - tains Roll down their gold - en sand;
Though ev - ery pros - pect pleas - es, And on - ly man is vile:
Shall we to men be - night - ed The lamp of life de - ny?
Till, like a sea of glo - ry, It spreads from pole to pole;

From ma - ny an an - cient riv - er, From ma - ny a palm - y plain,
In vain with lav - ish kind - ness The gifts of God are strown;
Sal - va - tion! Oh, sal - va - tion! The joy - ful sound pro - claim,
Till o'er our ran - somed na - ture The Lamb for sin - ners slain,

They call us to de - liv - er Their land from er - ror's chain.
The hea - then in his blind - ness Bows down to wood and stone.
Till earth's re - mot - est na - tion Has learned Mes - si - ah's Name.
Re - deem - er, King, Cre - a - tor, In bliss re - turns to reign. A - MEN.

WHENEVER you hear of *the* Missionary hymn, you may be sure the one above is meant. It is interesting to know how it came to be written. A royal letter had been sent to every church in England, asking that an offering be taken for missionary work in the East. Reginald Heber was visiting his father-in-law, the Dean of St. Asaph, at the time. Both were preparing sermons to be delivered on the following day, when the offering was to be taken. The Dean suggested that Heber write something to be sung at the service. While the others in the room were talking Heber went to a corner by himself, and in about twenty minutes wrote the first three stanzas of this hymn, later adding the fourth, which is its fitting climax.

It was hard to find music suitable for this hymn, as the rhythm is unusual. But one day a lady in Savannah heard of a young bank clerk near by who had written some very fine songs. So she sent her son with a copy of the words to see him, and in half an hour he returned with the beautiful music which we know so well. The bank clerk was no other than Lowell Mason, who later became so famous for his many fine hymns.

From Greenland's Icy Mountains

An Iceberg in the Far North   From Photograph by Warren Taylor

OW would you like to see a scene like this in the summertime? The ice floating on the water makes a very beautiful picture, but we may well imagine that it means danger too. Any ships that pass near by must be very careful, for the ice extends far under the water. And on the coast near at hand the ground is covered with ice and snow except for a short time in summer. It seems strange to us that any people should want to live in such a cold country, but scattered along the coast are many little villages of fishermen who know no other life.

These people need to know about Jesus as much as any of us do, but it is a hard life for any missionary who goes among them. Perhaps you have heard of Dr. Grenfell and others who are giving their lives in just such places as this. Going up and down the coast in hospital ships, or driving over the snow and ice on a sledge drawn by Eskimo dogs, they endure all sorts of hardships. Sometimes they spend hours, or even days, in the bitterest cold to reach some point where they may help a child who is sick. They have built hospitals, schools, and churches; and in every way try to show the fishermen that Jesus loves them and wants to help them in every part of their life.

Hark! the Voice of Jesus Calling

REV. DANIEL MARCH, 1868

J. W. ELLIOTT

1. Hark! the voice of Je - sus call - ing, "Who will go and work to - day?
2. If you can - not cross the o - cean, And the heath - en lands ex - plore,
3. Let none hear you i - dly say - ing, "There is noth - ing I can do,"

Fields are white and har - vests wait - ing; Who will bear the sheaves a - way?"
You can find the heath - en near - er, You can help them at your door.
While the souls of men are dy - ing, And the Mas - ter calls for you:

p VOICES IN UNISON   *cres.*

Loud and long the Mas - ter call - eth; Rich re - ward He of - fers free;
If you can - not give your thou - sands, You can give the wid - ow's mite;
Take the task He gives you glad - ly; Let His work your pleas - ure be;

f IN HARMONY

Who will an - swer, glad-ly say - ing, "Here am I, send me, send me?"
And the least you give for Je - sus Will be pre-cious in His sight.
An - swer quick - ly when He call-eth, "Here am I, send me, send me." A - MEN.

ONE day the Rev. Daniel March was asked to preach before the Young Men's Christian Association of Philadelphia. He carefully prepared his sermon, choosing his text from Isaiah, "Here am I, send me." He planned to have the hymns carry out the idea of this text, but at the last moment found that one of the hymns he had chosen was not suitable. In great haste he wrote the hymn above, and it was sung at the meeting from the slip of paper upon which he had written it.

Dr. March would probably have been astonished if he had been told that the sermon upon which he had worked so carefully would soon be forgotten, while this hymn would become one of our splendid missionary challenges. So far as we know this is the only hymn that Dr. March ever wrote. We wish he had written more.

Hark, the Voice of Jesus Calling

ERHAPS the story of Isaiah is not so familiar to you as many other parts of the Bible. He was one of the greatest prophets in the Old Testament. One day he went up to the Temple to worship. The king of Judah had just died, and the country was in a very serious condition. The wealthy citizens were forgetting God in their eagerness for more riches, and were cruel to the poor. Isaiah felt that unless his country returned to the ways of the Lord ruin was ahead. Suddenly he had a vision of God! His own sinfulness seemed to loom before him, but an angel placed a coal from the altar upon his lips, saying, "Thy sin is cleansed."

Isaiah   John S. Sargent

himself, even going barefoot through cold Judæan winters to make his message more effective.

In the picture we see him with arms uplifted, as if to bring his countrymen to a higher, better world. The light of hope is on his face, for he knew that, in spite of their sinful ways, One would come to save his country. Of that glad day he declared:

"Then the eyes of the blind shall be opened, and the ears of the deaf shall be unstopped. Then shall the lame man leap as an hart, and the tongue of the dumb sing." "The wolf also shall dwell with the lamb, and the leopard shall lie down with the kid; and the calf and the young lion and fatling together; and a little child shall lead them."

Then Isaiah heard the voice of the Lord saying, "Whom shall I send?" And he replied, "Here am I, send me."

Although he was but a young man at this time, he continued to preach with the greatest energy all his life, calling his people to obey the Lord. He was willing to sacrifice

This picture is part of a large painting of the prophets, made by John S. Sargent, one of our most famous American painters. It is upon the wall of the Boston Public Library.

Christic for the World We Sing

SAMUEL WOLCOTT, 1869

FELICE DE GIARDINI, 1769

1. Christ for the world we sing; The world to Christ we bring
2. Christ for the world we sing; The world to Christ we bring
3. Christ for the world we sing; The world to Christ we bring

With lov - ing zeal; The poor, and them that mourn, The faint and
With fer - vent prayer; The way - ward and the lost, By rest - less
With one ac - cord; With us the work to share, With us re -

o - ver-borne, Sin - sick and sor - row-worn, Whom Christ doth heal.
pas- sion tossed, Re-deemed at count-less cost From dark de - spair.
proach to dare, With us the Cross to bear For Christ our Lord. A - MEN.

AT one time there was a large meeting held by the Young Men's Christian Association in Cleveland. Right over the platform, in letters of evergreen, was this challenge: "Christ for the World, and the World for Christ." At the convention a minister, Samuel Wolcott, was very much impressed by these words. When a young man he had himself been a missionary in Syria, but had been forced to return to America on account of his health. He had, however, always been an enthusiastic worker for missions. He had never written much, and now he was fifty-five years old, but the force of this motto appealed to him, and he felt that he must write a hymn that would preserve it. On his way home from the first meeting, as he was walking by himself in the street, he composed the words given above. This was his first attempt, but we know how well he succeeded, for the hymn above has become one of our most popular missionary hymns.

Starting with this hymn Samuel Wolcott wrote others, and in a few years had written over two hundred.

Christic for the World We Sing

As Jesus was going up into heaven, He gave as His last words the command, "Ye shall be witnesses unto me . . .unto the uttermost part of the earth," words which have ever since been a missionary challenge to His followers.

It seems strange that we should be so slow in grasping the meaning of a statement made so clearly, but it has been nearly two thousand years since Jesus lived, and there are still many sections of the world where people have had no opportunity to know about Christ.

In the picture we see Him as

The Ascension

Gottlieb Biermann

we see just a suggestion of soft light around Jesus' head.

It is remarkable how the artist has represented the ascension of Jesus, mostly by means of the folds of His garments. It seems almost as though a wind from below were helping to carry Him toward heaven.

There is almost a look of sadness about Christ's face as He is quietly slipping away from amongst His friends. He seems to long to be with them in person and to help them directly in their work of spreading His teaching. Perhaps He is thinking of the hard-

He is parting from His friends. This is not done in a spectacular way; there are no crowds of angels attending, and Jesus is not glorified by halos or by any other sign of His power. We must look very closely before ships and difficulties they will face. His arms are outstretched as though to bless them and to assure them that, though they shall no longer see Him, yet His spirit will be with them.

The Son of God Goes Forth to War

REGINALD HEBER, 1827   HENRY S. CUTLER, 1872

1. The Son of God goes forth to war, A king-ly crown to gain;
2. The mar-tyr first, whose ea-gle eye Could pierce be-yond the grave,
3. A glo-rious band, the cho-sen few On whom the Spir-it came;
4. A no-ble ar-my—men and boys, The ma-tron and the maid,

His blood-red ban-ner streams a-far; Who fol-lows in His train?
Who saw his Mas-ter in the sky, And called on Him to save;
Twelve val-iant saints, their hope they knew, And mocked the cross and flame;
A-round the Sav-iour's throne re-joice, In robes of light ar-rayed:

Who best can drink His cup of woe, Tri-umph-ant o-ver pain;
Like Him, with par-don on his tongue, In midst of mor-tal pain,
They met the ty-rant's bran-dished steel, The li-on's gor-y mane;
They climbed the steep as-cent of heav'n Thro' per-il, toil, and pain:

Who pa-tient bears his cross be-low— He fol-lows in His train.
He prayed for them that did the wrong: Who fol-lows in his train?
They bowed their necks the stroke to feel: Who fol-lows in their train?
O God, to us may grace be given To fol-low in their train! A-MEN.

THIS is one of the most rousing missionary hymns that we have. It is a direct challenge to sacrifice everything in order to follow Christ, even if it should mean death by the sword, the flame, or wild beasts. It is no easy life that is offered! Reginald Heber wrote this hymn for a service to be held on St. Stephen's Day. In the second verse, where he speaks of "the martyr," he is directly referring to the triumphant death of Stephen. All through the hymn we find references to the twelve Apostles and to others who have given their lives for Christ.

And Heber himself "followed in their train," for when the call came to him from India he left home and friends, and went there as a Missionary Bishop. After three years of splendid work he died there in active service.

The Son of God Goes Forth to War

THIS picture is familiar, I am sure, for it is placed so often in schoolrooms and public buildings. It represents Sir Galahad, a noble youth, starting out on his life-work. He has decided that the greatest service that he can perform is to search for the Holy Grail, or cup, which Jesus used at the Last Supper with His disciples. This cup was kept in a castle, where only those who were pure could see it. For a long time there had not been anyone who was good enough to see it, and people were afraid that it was lost. Those who lived in the Castle of the Holy Grail were suffering as a consequence.

Sir Galahad journeyed far and wide, performing many deeds of bravery, and helping many who were in distress. He was often tempted by his enemies, but he kept himself true, and at last after many years was rewarded by a sight of the Grail, and relieved those in the castle from their suffering.

Sir Galahad

G. F. Watts

In the picture we see him as he is setting out upon his travels. He is well prepared, for he is clad in full armor. The wonderful sword by his side came from out of a rock. It had been seen by many people, but no one had been strong enough to draw it out until Sir Galahad had tried. His magnificent horse stands ready to start at any time. Yet before mounting his steed he pauses for a moment for prayer. He is not proud and overconfident that he will succeed where others have failed, but goes forth in humility and earnestness.

The artist, Watts, is one of England's finest painters. He believed that pictures should be painted, not for pleasure or amusement, but for some definite service.

In Christ There Is No East or West

JOHN OXENHAM, 1908

ALEXANDER R. REINAGLE, 1826

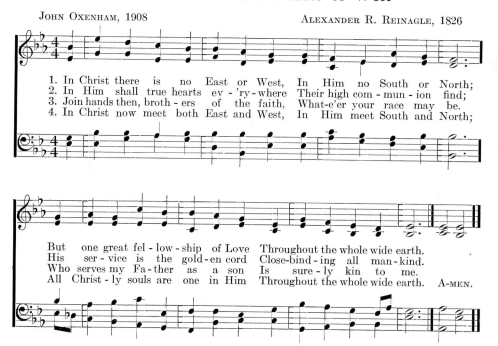

1. In Christ there is no East or West, In Him no South or North;
2. In Him shall true hearts ev-'ry-where Their high com-mun-ion find;
3. Join hands then, broth-ers of the faith, What-e'er your race may be.
4. In Christ now meet both East and West, In Him meet South and North;

But one great fel-low-ship of Love Throughout the whole wide earth.
His ser-vice is the gold-en cord Close-bind-ing all man-kind.
Who serves my Fa-ther as a son Is sure-ly kin to me.
All Christ-ly souls are one in Him Throughout the whole wide earth. A-MEN.

THE talent of John Oxenham as a writer was not recognized so early as one might expect. After finishing his schooling in England, Oxenham went into business, and lived for some years in France, and the United States of America. He also traveled over the greater part of Europe, and in North America, from Canada to the southern states, where he considered taking up the business of orange-growing. Unconsciously this traveling was giving him a contact with people and a breadth of vision which has been invaluable later on.

Returning to England, Oxenham took up writing in spare time as business permitted. But finding his ability in this direction, he has gradually given up business, and has devoted himself to writing. Oxenham loves to be out of doors, climbing mountains, and rowing on the rivers, where he can see the beauties of the wonderful world which God has made.

His poem given above, which is used as a hymn, has been dramatized very effectively. A cross in the center of the platform represents the spirit of Christ, and from the four corners come representatives of the nations of the world. They kneel before the cross, present gifts, and join hands during the singing of the stanzas, showing in a dramatic way the thought of the hymn, that we are all brothers in Christ.

A copy of Thorwaldsen's statue of the Christ stands at the entrance of the Johns Hopkins Hospital, in Baltimore. With arms outstretched as if to welcome those from every quarter of the globe, rich or poor, regardless of race or creed, this monument seems to truly represent the Universal Christ.

In Christ There Is No East or West

Christ the Consoler

Bertel Thorwaldsen

BERTEL THORWALDSEN was the son of a wood-carver from Iceland who had settled in Denmark. As a boy Thorwaldsen helped his father with his work, and showed so much skill that at the age of eleven years he was sent to the School of Art for further study. Here his talent was recognized, and he won a scholarship which took him to Rome. For twenty-three years he remained in Italy studying the works of the great masters of art. Gradually his own ability became recognized. It was he who made the model for the famous "Lion of Lucerne."

One day a commission came to him to make a series of colossal statues of Christ and the Twelve Apostles for a church in Copenhagen, his native city. So he returned to Denmark to make the plans for the statue shown above, called "Christ the Consoler."

Thorwaldsen left his fortune for a museum in Copenhagen which contains many of the drawings and models for his works. By his own request he was buried in the courtyard of the museum, under a bed of roses.

Ring Out the Old, Ring In the New

Alfred Tennyson, 1850

J. Baptiste Calkin, 1872

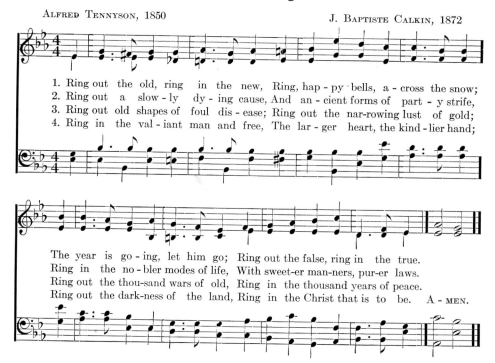

1. Ring out the old, ring in the new, Ring, hap - py bells, a - cross the snow;
2. Ring out a slow - ly dy - ing cause, And an - cient forms of part - y strife,
3. Ring out old shapes of foul dis - ease; Ring out the nar-rowing lust of gold;
4. Ring in the val - iant man and free, The lar - ger heart, the kind - lier hand;

The year is go - ing, let him go; Ring out the false, ring in the true.
Ring in the no - bler modes of life, With sweet-er man-ners, pur-er laws.
Ring out the thou-sand wars of old, Ring in the thousand years of peace.
Ring out the dark-ness of the land, Ring in the Christ that is to be. A - men.

PERHAPS you recognize these stanzas as coming from one of the greatest of poems, "In Memoriam." This poem was written by Alfred Tennyson in memory of his friend, Arthur Hallam, with whom he had been closely associated at Cambridge University, England. Hallam was a young poet of great promise, who was engaged to be married to Tennyson's sister. His sudden death caused Tennyson to grieve for many years, and brought forth his immortal poem on life and death. The stanzas used in this hymn occur near the close of the poem. They sound the note of confident faith, and challenge all to the highest in life.

Many honors came to Tennyson during his lifetime, among them that of being chosen Poet Laureate of England. Yet his heart remained true and unaffected; his association with rulers and princes did not keep him from loving children; and with his lofty ideals he enjoyed the common things of life, and had a keen sense of humor. There is a story that one day, as Tennyson was out driving with a little girl, she suggested that they change hats. Tennyson entered into the play, and it was hard to tell which looked the queerer, the little girl with the huge stovepipe hat, coming down almost to her shoulders, or the dignified poet, with a tiny lace and rosebud bonnet tied under his chin with a bit of ribbon. Both enjoyed the smiles of those whom they passed.

While Tennyson wrote a number of very long poems, such as "In Memoriam," he also had the art of giving a great message in very few words. What child, or what older person as well, does not love the verses that begin,

"Little flower in the crannied wall"?

Ring Out the Old, Ring In the New

Copyright Curtis Publishing Company, Courtesy *Ladies' Home Journal*   Jules Guerin
The Church at Sleepy Hollow

E do not wonder that the lighted church, throwing its soft rays through the stained-glass windows across the snow, appealed to the artist, Jules Guerin, as the subject for a picture. Little churches have played an important part in the making of our country. And the ringing of bells on Christmas and New Year's Eve has been a challenge to many, as it was to Tennyson, to give up baser things, and seek "the nobler modes of life, with sweeter manners, purer laws."

This Dutch Church at Tarrytown on the Hudson, about twenty-five miles above New York City, is an old historic building, erected in 1685. The bricks in the chimney, and the flat yellow ones around the windows, and the bell were all brought over from Holland. Stone walls thirty inches thick assure us that this church was intended to endure. The high windows seven feet from the ground were at one time protected by iron bars. The church is very plain within, having a huge pulpit and seats without backs.

Washington Irving, one of our first great American writers, has immortalized this region in his *Legend of Sleepy Hollow*. Of this church he says, "It stands on a knoll, surrounded by locust trees, almost rectangular, hip roof, small belfry, and at either end vanes as old as itself." Irving now lies in the graveyard of this church.

The original of this painting hangs in a corridor of the building of the Curtis Publishing Company, in Philadelphia. Jules Guerin is well known as a mural painter, and his works are to be found in the foremost cities of the United States. Born in St. Louis, Guerin studied at the Beaux Arts, in Paris, receiving many medals for his productions. He painted decorations for the Lincoln Memorial Building in Washington. Other mural paintings of his may be seen in various banks and railroad stations from New York to San Francisco.

Jesus Shall Reign Where'er the Sun

ISAAC WATTS, 1719   JOHN HATTON,   –1793

1. Je - sus shall reign wher - e'er the sun Does his suc - ces - sive
2. For Him shall end - less prayer be made, And prais - es throng to
3. Peo - ple and realms of ev - ery tongue Dwell on His love with
4. Bless - ings a - bound wher - e'er He reigns; The pris - oner leaps to
5. Let ev - ery crea - ture rise and bring Pe - cul - iar hon - ors

jour - neys run; His king - dom spread from shore to shore,
crown His head; His name, like sweet per - fume, shall rise
sweet - est song, And in - fant voic - es shall pro - claim
loose his chains, The wea - ry find e - ter - nal rest,
to our King; An - gels de - scend with songs a - gain,

Till moons shall wax and wane no more.
With ev - ery morn - ing sac - ri - fice;
Their ear - ly bless - ings on His name.
And all the sons of want are blest.
And earth re - peat the loud A - men! A - MEN.

THIS hymn, originally written as one of praise, is now being used as a missionary challenge. As is the case with nearly all of Watts' hymns, it is based on a psalm; in
this instance on portions of the seventy-second:

> "He shall have dominion also from sea to sea, . . ."
> "His name shall be continued as long as the sun."

G. J. Stevenson, in his *Notes on the Methodist Hymn Book*, says of this hymn:

Perhaps one of the most interesting occasions on which this hymn was used
was that on which King George the Sable, of the South Sea Islands, but of blessed
memory, gave a new constitution to his people, exchanging a heathen for a Christian
form of government. Under the spreading branches of the banyan trees sat some
natives from Tonga, Fiji, and Samoa, on Whitsunday, 1862, assembled for divine
worship. The solemn service began by the entire audience singing Dr. Watts' hymn:

> "Jesus shall reign where'er the sun
> Doth his successive journeys run!"

That was indeed Christ's kingdom set up in the earth.

The music to which the hymn is sung is an old English tune called "Duke Street." Like
many of the other English tunes it was named from a street with which it was associated.

Jesus Shall Reign Where'er the Sun

Mateo Alonso

The Christ of the Andes

CHRIST OF EVERYWHERE

"Christ of the Andes," Christ of Every-
 where,
Great lover of the hills, the open air,
And patient lover of impatient men
Who blindly strive and sin and strive
 again,—
Thou Living Word, larger than any creed,
Thou Love Divine, uttered in human
 deed,—
Oh, teach the world, warring and wander-
 ing still,
Thy way of Peace, the footpath of Good
 Will!

HENRY VAN DYKE
(Used by the author's permission)

❧ ❧ ❧

IN one of the remote corners of the earth stands this statue of the Christ. High in the Andes Mountains it is placed on the border between Argentina and Chile. Some time ago these two countries were not friends, but were preparing for war. The boundary between them was supposed to run along the top of the mountains, but the two nations could not agree as to just where this dividing line lay.

In Argentina a bishop named Benavente felt that it was wrong to cause bloodshed, and that, after all, fighting would not show where the top of the mountains lay. With the help of Bishop Java, in Chile, who felt as he did, he induced the two countries to settle their dispute in a peaceful and Christian manner by having a friend of both nations fix the line for them. When the line was determined there was great rejoicing. This statue, planned by an Argentine sculptor, was cast in bronze melted down from cannon. On it are inscribed the words:

"Sooner shall these mountains crumble into dust than the people of Argentina and Chile break the peace which they have sworn to maintain at the feet of Christ the Redeemer."

This statue stands as one of the great triumphs of Christianity. A reproduction of it has been placed in the Peace Palace at The Hague, Holland.

Some of God's Laws

And God spake all these words, saying,

I am the Lord thy God, which brought thee out of the land of Egypt, out of the house of bondage.

Thou shalt have no other gods before Me.

Thou shalt not make unto thee any graven image.

Thou shat not take the name of the Lord thy God in vain.

Remember the Sabbath day, to keep it holy.

Honor thy father and thy mother.

Thou shalt not kill.

Thou shalt not commit adultery.

Thou shalt not steal.

Thou shalt not bear false witness against thy neighbor.

Thou shalt not covet.

(Also the two commandments that Jesus gave:)

Thou shalt love the Lord thy God with all thy heart, and with all thy soul, and with all thy mind, and with all thy strength.

Thou shalt love thy neighbor as thyself.

From BEETHOVEN

Lord, have mer - cy up - on.... us, And in - cline our hearts to keep this law.

(This response to be sung after each commandment)

THE music for this response was written by Beethoven, perhaps the greatest composer that the world has ever known. When but a small boy he showed great ability for music. Not only could he play the piano, but he learned a number of other instruments as well. Perhaps that is why later on he was able to write such splendid music for orchestras.

When Beethoven was still a young man his hearing began to fail. For one who loved music as he did, can you imagine anything more terrible? He carried an ear-trumpet, and had a piano with additional wires made especially for him. But as time went on he could not hear even the loudest sounds. Yet he did not give up. He kept on writing music as he walked in the fields, or sat at his desk. He could do this, hard as it was, for he had learned to hear his own music in his thoughts.

Does not the statue of Moses on the opposite page impress you with his greatness as a leader? How strong he is, how upright in his bearing! It is not hard for us to see why God chose such a man to lead the Israelites out of Egypt, and guided him in law-making. On the two tablets of stone which he has by his side are written the Ten Commandments, upon which all our law is based. God has just given these laws to Moses on Mount Sinai, and now, as he is coming down the mountain he sees the Israelites worshiping a golden calf! No wonder he starts with horror at such a sight! Every muscle in his body is tense as he is struggling to restrain his anger.

The Commandments

O artist, unless possibly Leonardo, has been gifted in more ways than Michelangelo, called Michel the Angel. He was a painter, architect, engineer, poet, and musician. But more than anything else he loved to carve statues, huge gigantic ones that impress us with their strength rather than their beauty. "Let me carve a mountain," was his cry.

When a child he had for a nurse the wife of a stonemason, and probably Michelangelo's first love for sculpture came from playing near the quarry and watching the stonemasons at work. His life was not a happy one, for he was continually having one misfortune after another. As a young man his nose was broken, which disfigured his looks, and as he loved beautiful things, this was always a trial to him.

Moses   Michelangelo

Then, he was continually hindered in his work, rarely being allowed to finish it as he wished. This very statue was to be one of a group for the tomb of Pope Julius. But after Michelangelo had started, Julius was told that he should not have his tomb made before he died, so Michelangelo was ordered to stop.

But in spite of all obstacles, Michelangelo has left us some of our very finest statues since the time of the Greeks. It has been said that this statue represents Michelangelo's own spirit, his struggle to restrain himself.

Praise God from Whom All Blessings Flow

THOMAS KEN, 1692   LOUIS BOURGEOIS, 1551

Praise God, from whom all bless - ings flow; Praise Him, all crea-tures here be - low;

Praise Him a - bove, ye heav'nly host; Praise Father, Son, and Ho - ly Ghost. A-MEN.

PROBABLY these words are sung more frequently in church than any others. They were written as the closing stanza of Bishop Ken's three famous hymns, "For Morning, Evening, and Midnight," composed for the students of Winchester College, England. Several copies were printed on sheets and hung on the walls of the dormitories, where the boys could see them the first thing in the morning and the last thing at night.

Bishop Ken himself was a great true-hearted Englishman. He was firm in his convictions, whatever it might cost him. He did not hesitate to reprove even the king himself, in the plainest manner, for his sins. At one time the king was planning to visit his town and wished to quarter some of his followers in Bishop Ken's home. The bishop knew that these people were not leading honest lives, and felt it would be a disgrace to have them in his home, so he refused. But the messengers of the king would not take "No" for an answer. Whereupon Ken immediately had some repairs made upon his house, and when the followers arrived they found that the roof had been taken off, so they were forced to go elsewhere.

At another time he was ordered by the king to read a Declaration of Indulgence. He felt that it was wrong, and he refused to do it, even though he was imprisoned in the Tower of London for refusing. Toward the end of his life he was reduced to poverty. But this he did not mind, for he had never been attracted by the wealth and luxury of the Court. At his own request six of the poorest men of the community were selected to be his pallbearers, and his funeral was without display of any kind.

This doxology has been sung upon many important occasions. During the Civil War it was a great source of comfort to our boys in Libby Prison.

The tune is a very old one, receiving its name because it was used with the one hundredth psalm (Some say one hundred thirty-fourth.) of the *Geneva Psalter*.

134

The Doxology

T would be hard to imagine a more beautiful angel. How gracefully he is floating upon a cloud, ready to use the trumpet in his hand in praise of God! What beautiful embroidery is upon the robe! Do you see the little tongue of fire upon his brow, and the lovely ornaments in the halo?

This painting was made long ago by a monk who lived in Florence, Italy. When a boy he was called Guido. He loved to paint, and wanted to become an artist; but one day he heard a great preacher who was urging everyone to become more holy. Guido was very much impressed, and decided that he would become a monk and live in a convent. But he still loved to paint, and whenever he had the opportunity he decorated the walls of churches with beautiful pictures.

Angel
Fra Angelico

Because he painted such lovely angels he has been called Fra Angelico. So often angels are represented as dressed in pure white, but Fra Angelico made gorgeous colored robes and decorated the wings, halo, and background profusely with gold. Before painting each picture he prayed and fasted. Many of his paintings are on the walls of the Convent of San Marco, in Florence.

Fra Angelico had no idea that anyone except his brother monks would ever see his works, so he painted purely for the glory of God, and to remind his brother monks of their religious duties. In one room he painted St. Peter with his finger to his lips, showing that silence must be kept in that room. And in each of the cells he painted a little scene from the life of Christ, to help the monks keep their minds upon holy subjects.

For years few people but the monks looked upon his works. But after four hundred years the Convent of San Marco was made by the government into a museum, and now thousands of visitors every year are able to see these beautiful paintings.

Michelangelo said of Fra Angelico, "Surely our good brother was allowed to visit Paradise and copy the angels there."

A Closing Word for the Boys and Girls

Let this book be just a beginning of your study of hymns, with pictures which bring out their meaning. You will be surprised to find what a large field is open before you. Several pages are left vacant at the end of this book in which you may insert some of your favorite hymns. Perhaps you will find an evening scene which illustrates "Day Is Dying in the West." A picture of Grace Darling and her father in a life-boat is most appropriate for "Throw Out the Life Line." A view of the rock of Gibraltar is not hard to obtain, and what could be more suitable for the splendid hymn, "My Hope Is Built on Nothing Less," with the ringing chorus, "On Christ, the Solid Rock, I Stand"? Many others will occur to you and among them a photograph of your own church might be used for "I Love Thy Kingdom, Lord, the Place of Thine Abode."